urban scrawl

urban scrawl

THE WORLD AS SEEN THROUGH THE BEMUSED EYES OF

Erika Ritter

Macmillan of Canada
A DIVISION OF GAGE PUBLISHING LIMITED
Toronto, Canada

Canadian Cataloguing in Publication Data

Ritter, Erika, date.
 Urban scrawl

ISBN 0-7715-9810-6

1. Canadian wit and humor (English)* 2. Canada—
Social life and customs—1965-   —Anecdotes,
facetiae, satire, etc.* I. Title.

PS8585.I88U7 1984   C818'.5407   C84-098967-9
PR9199.3.R587U7 1984

"The Catcher in the Rye-and-Water" first appeared in *Toronto Life*, and "Purse-onally Speaking", "Mangiamania", and "The Dirty Thirties" were first published in *City Woman*. Other selections have appeared in a different form in *City Woman* and on CBC-Radio's *Morningside*. The majority of pieces originated as items on the author's weekly "Adult Phenomena" segment on CBC-Radio's *Stereo Morning*, to which program the author offers grateful acknowledgement.

Edited by Maggie MacDonald
Designed by Leslie Smart and Associates
Cover photos by Norman Scudellari

Macmillan of Canada
A Division of Gage Publishing Limited

Printed in Canada

For my mother,
who made the mistake
of encouraging
this kind of thing

CONTENTS

bicycles

It wasn't always like this. There was a time in the life of the world when adults were adults, having firmly put away childish things and thrown away the key.

Not any more. The change must have come about innocently enough, I imagine. Modern Man learning to play nicely in the sandbox with the other grown-ups. Very low-tension stuff.

Now, in every direction you look, your gaze is met by the risible spectacle of adults postponing adolescence well into senility by means of adult toys: running shoes, baseball bats, roller skates, and – bicycles!

But the attitude is no longer the fun-loving approach of a bunch of superannuated kids, and I'm sure you can envision how the evolution occurred. Jogging progressed from a casual encounter with the fresh air to an intensive relationship, attended by sixty-dollar jogging shoes and a designer sweatband. Playing baseball stopped being fun unless you had a Lacoste (as opposed to low-cost) tee-shirt in which to impress your teammates. And where was the thrill in running around a squash court unless it was with a potentially important client?

As for bicycles – well, let's not even talk about bicycles. On the other hand, maybe we *should* talk about them, because there's something particularly poignant about how it all went wrong for the bicycle, by what declension this once proud and carefree vehicle sank into the role of beast of burden, to bear the weight of sobersided grown-ups at their supposed sport.

First, there was the earliest domestication of the North American bicycle (*cyclus pedalis americanus*) in the late Hippie Scene Era of the 1960s. This was the age of the no-nuke whole-grain cyclist, who saw in the bicycle the possibility of Making a Statement while he rode. A statement about pollution, about materialism, about imperialism, about militarism, about – enough already. You get the picture: two wheels good, four wheels bad.

Thus it was that the basic bicycle gradually evolved into a chunky three-speed number from China, bowed down under a plastic kiddie carrier, army surplus knapsacks, and a faded fender-sticker advising Make Tofu, Not War. And a rider clad in a red plaid lumber-jacket, Birkenstock sandals, and an expression of urgent concern for all living things.

Once the very act of bicycle riding had become an act of high moral purpose, it was an easy step to the next phase of the bicycle's journey along the path of post-Meanderthal seriousness.

I'm speaking of the era of the high-strung thoroughbred bicycle, whose rider had also made advances, from pedalling peacenik to a hunched and humorless habitué of the velodrome, clad in leather-seated shorts, white crash helmet, and fingerless gloves, whizzing soundlessly, and with no hint of joy, down city streets and along the shoulders of super-highways, aboard a vehicle sculpted in wisps of silver chrome. A vehicle so overbred, in its final evolutionary stages, that it began to resemble the mere exoskeleton of a conventional cycle, its flesh picked away by birds of carrion.

Having been stripped of any connection with its innocent and leisurely origins, the bicycle now no longer bore the slightest resemblance to the happy creature it once had been. And in the mid-Plastic Scene Era, another crippling blow was struck by the upscale name-brand cyclist, who came along to finish what the fanatical velodromist had refined. Namely, the complete transformation of an ambling and unhurried mode of transit into a fast, nerve-wracking, expensive, and utterly competitive display of high speed, high technology, and high status.

The Upscale Cyclist was looking for a twelve-speed Bottecchia that matched his eyes, something that he'd look trendy upon the seat of, when riding to the office (the office!), and he was ready to pay in four figures for it.

Not only that, he was also prepared to shell out some heavy bread for those status accessories to complete the picture: the backpack designed by the engineers at NASA, the insulated water-bottle to keep his Perrier chilled just right, the sixteen-track Walkman that would virtually assure him the envy of all his friends.

So much for the cyclist. What of his poor debased mount?

Not surprisingly, amongst the breed of bicycle, morale is currently low, and personal pride all but a thing of the past. And yet... and yet, there are those who say that *cyclus pedalis americanus* is an indomitable creature, and that it is the bicycle, not its rider, who will make the last evolution of the wheel.

In fact, some theorize that the present high incidence of bicycle thievery, far from being evidence of crime, is actually an indication that the modern bicycle has had enough of oppressive exploitation and man's joyless ways, and is in the process of reverting to the wild in greater and greater numbers.

There have always remained a few aboriginal undomesticated bicycles – or so the theory goes – and now it is these free-spirited mavericks, down from the hills at night, who visit urban bike-racks, garages, and back porches to lure tame bicycles away with them.

Costly Kryptonite locks are wrenched asunder, expensive accoutrements are shrugged off, intricate gear systems are torn away, and lo – look what is revealed! Unadorned, undefiled *cyclus* in all his pristine glory, unfettered and unencumbered once more, and free to roam.

A wistful fantasy, you might say? The maundering illusions of someone who's been riding her bicycle too long without a crash helmet? I wonder.

Just the other day, there was that piece in the paper about a bicycle that went berserk in a shopping centre, smashing two display windows before it was subdued. And did you hear about the recent sighting of a whole herd of riderless bicycles, all rolling soundlessly across a park in the night?

It all kind of gets you to thinking. I mean, do *you* know where your ten-speed is tonight?

Club Dread

Dear Diary: My first day of holiday, and I hardly know where to begin recording my impressions. Forgive the shakiness of my handwriting in this, the first entry in my brand-new "Vacation Journal". I don't know which is more responsible for the unsteadiness of my script – the pounding of my excited heart, or the bouncing over the rutted tropical roads of our bus, bearing us from the airport to the site of our exotic once-in-a-lifetime vacation here on Ecstasy Island.

Some of my fellow travellers have already begun to grumble a little, particularly those whose luggage did not, for some inexplicable reason, make the transition from the airport at home to the Ecstasy Island terminal, where we landed less than an hour ago.

Whereas I can imagine the unpleasantness of jouncing along (the bus seems not to be equipped with springs) a dirt road in ninety-eight-degree heat (nor does the bus appear to have air-conditioning, and all the windows are welded shut) clad in wool sweaters, corduroy slacks, and snow boots, it does seem to me a trifle rash of my new companions not to have anticipated the possibility of baggage loss by packing a change of light-weight clothes in their carry-on baggage, only some of which was stolen at the refuelling stop.

True – as my new-found friends, a delightful couple by the name of Braithwaite, pointed out to me with jovial smiles as we boarded the bus – the fact that the Ecstasy Island Beach Club facilities are located one hundred and fifty miles from the airport is nowhere mentioned in any of the club's promotional literature.

None of us was therefore expecting this long overland trek under a blazing sun.

However, I intend to take a leaf from the Braithwaites' philosophical book and accept this small reversal with equanimity, just as I accepted our aircraft's unscheduled stops in: Montreal; Halifax; Bangor, Maine; Wilmington, Delaware; the Dallas–Fort Worth Airport; and Mexico City on the way down here, which have, by my rough calculation, lopped approximately thirty-three hours off our precious vacation time.

As I cast my eyes about at the unfamiliar (and flushed) faces all around me, it is astonishing to conjecture that we all will be, by holiday's end, fast friends, or even . . . ? Well, who can say?

There's a young man directly across the aisle from me, and though at the moment he's sweating profusely in a flannel shirt and heavy slacks, and still bleeding slightly from a chance blow on the forehead by a falling piece of fuselage panelling that occurred during a particularly nasty bit of turbulence over Gander (how it was we came to be over Gander in the first place, I no longer remember), I can see that he's essentially very good-looking, and would probably have a kindly expression, were it not for the fact that his face is contorted with pain. I shall investigate him further upon arrival. . . .

Meantime, I shall leave off writing for the present, as the Braithwaites are imploring me to enter into a game of Botticelli with them to pass the time, and as the effort of focussing my attention on the paper in the erratically moving bus is making me feel ever so slightly nauseated. More anon.

Well, it's anon, we are all settled in quarters at the Beach Club, and I can't help being certain I'm going to like it here. While the club brochure *did* promise that we would all be in single accommodation, I very much like the looks of my three roommates, and I really feel I could have done far worse. This way, at any rate, there is no possible danger of ever feeling lonely.

The Braithwaites are of the same cheerful opinion, although I detect a certain disappointed surprise in their discovery that they will not be sharing a room with each other. A number of other couples have suffered the same fate, and I must say, few are taking the situation as philosophically as the Braithwaites are.

"My goodness," Mrs. Braithwaite was heard to remark to the

four other ladies she is sharing with, "it'll be like one long pyjama party, that's what. After all, we can sleep with our husbands at home."

Unfortunately, none of the other ladies appeared to have heard what she said, for not one of them responded.

I have been down to the dining lounge for my first meal, armed with the sea-shell currency that is used here in lieu of cash. (Good thing, too, as much of my cash disappeared unaccountably from my room before I could get it into the club safe.) While I find the denominations of the shells somewhat confusing – I believe there are approximately four abalones to the U.S. dollar – I was still able to purchase some melon, which was very tasty if a little green, and a modest portion of rice for the rough equivalent of $8.35 American.

It seemed a little steep to me, especially as one of the kitchen staff remarked to me that my lunch cost more than he earns in a year, but perhaps I have simply made a mistake in the arithmetical conversion.

I had hoped, I must blushingly confess, for a glimpse of the good-looking young man I noted on the bus, but he was nowhere to be seen. Rumor around the lunch tables (located right under the broiling eye of the sun for some reason that none of us can understand) has it that he is in the club infirmary, suffering from a slight fever and a mild concussion, and I fervently trust that his injuries are no more serious than that. So far I have not noticed any other prospective male companions.

There was a rather paunchy and baldish gentleman in the drinks line-up beside me who complained vigorously that the so-called "unlimited free cocktails" available at lunch consist entirely of glasses of tepid tomato juice over which the vodka bottle has been languidly waved.

Then, when I went back for dessert (another piece of unripe melon that cost me thirteen abalone shells), there was another apparently unattached fellow with very bad acne scars who commented to me that, at the prices we were paying, it was a scandal to be served canned mango in the tropics.

If this is a sampling of the general calibre of single man available here in this group, then I must say I'm less disturbed than I was originally when one of my roommates, Rusty-Jean, told me the female-to-male ratio at the Beach Club is eight to one.

Rusty-Jean herself professes not to care about the marked scarcity of what she refers to as "hot pastrami", since, she says, she really came down here to catch up on her reading. As far as I can see from the pile of magazines on her portion of the end-table we all share, Rusty-Jean's reading runs heavily to *Hot Rod* and *Police Gazette*.

I find myself liking her, though, in spite of the tattoos.

Never a dull moment here on Ecstasy Island. After dinner tonight, Mr. Krieg, the head social director, was introduced by his second-in-command, Mr. Crispin. All heads turned to observe the entrance of the man upon whom so much of our holiday fate depends. A fine upright figure of a man is Mr. Krieg, and he is reputed by some experienced Ecstasy Island vacationers at my table to be "tough but fair".

However, later on I heard from good Mrs. Braithwaite (poor lady, in spite of her unfailing cheeriness, she seems somewhat ostracized by the other women she shares the suite with) that she had overheard some people murmuring about rumors to the effect that there had been a "vacationer rebellion" at the Beach Club to which Mr. Krieg had been previously assigned.

Of course, Mrs. Braithwaite and I pray these stories are unfounded. However, I must say I *did* detect an undercurrent of sternness in Mr. Krieg's welcoming address. "You are all here to have fun, fun, fun," he advised us. "Fun and nothing but fun. Am I right?"

And when the assembled multitude could muster nothing more than an apathetic "Right!" by way of response, I am certain that I saw a vein in Mr. Krieg's forehead begin to stand out, as he smiled in a set way and began to chivvy us: "Boy oh boy. You know, when my Uncle Earl had been buried for four days, he had more life in him than you folks. Listen, there's no room for party-poops here on the island. . . . "

Then he went on to enumerate what sounded, to my inexperienced ears at any rate, like a downright punishing schedule of sports activities and social events planned for our stay at the club, including a theme dance every night in the ballroom, compulsory disco lessons, mixed scuba diving, nude sunbathing, hikes to the Hanging Rock...

At length, when it seemed that Mr. Krieg's roster might never come to an end, Mr. Crispin (I like the looks of *him*, I must say) stepped in firmly to say, "Now, then, Mr. Krieg. Save something to tell them about tomorrow night, hm?"

There was a general laugh at that good-natured sally, from everyone except Mr. Krieg, whose vein seemed to protrude even more prominently. He snarled out through clenched teeth that tonight's dance would have a Roaring Twenties theme, before turning on his heel to stride wordlessly out of the dining lounge, with Mr. Crispin following slowly and somewhat meditatively behind him.

I have had no chance to make comparisons at length with anyone else concerning first impressions of the social director and his assistant, because as soon as dinner was over, Mrs. Braithwaite began tugging at my sleeve. Dear sweet lady though she is, I found myself sounding a trifle impatient as I advised her that this was no time to propose a game of Botticelli, or a round of Boggle, of which she is also fond.

But, as it turned out, what she wanted was for me to help her try to locate Mr. Braithwaite, whom she has not seen since lunch.

Much as I tried to assure her that her husband would likely show up in due course, since there is no way off the island (as some of the more disenchanted were heard to repeat over dinner, which once again consisted of melons and rice), the poor woman seemed quite insistent that I accompany her on a search of the two dancing areas, the games room, and the beach.

Although Mr. Braithwaite was not in evidence in any of these localities, I did make some other discoveries of more than passing interest. One was stumbling upon one of my roommates, Tharma, in a violent clinch under a palm tree with the pitted young man who'd been complaining about the canned mangoes at lunch.

The other was virtually running into my tattooed friend Rusty-Jean seated on a remote stretch of sand with the young man I'd spotted on the bus, who now sports a wide white bandage across his injured forehead – which was, in the bright tropical moon-light, the first thing that drew my attention to the spot where he and Rusty-Jean were seated.

Well, dear diary, what can I say, except that I am sorely disappointed? Much as I have warmed to Rusty-Jean, leather wristbands and all, I would never have tapped her as a possible rival for the affections of that particular young man, who looks more like a fan of *Canadian Forum* than of *Police Gazette*.

His evident but totally baffling interest in the muscular Rusty-Jean I can only ascribe to one of the following: some sort of perverse fascination on his part with tattoos; the strong likelihood that he is still concussed, and may indeed by this time even be slightly delirious; or the fact that, when Mr. Braithwaite and I came upon them, Rusty-Jean was in the process of passing to him the most enormous marijuana cigarette that I have ever seen.

"Oh look," said Mrs. Braithwaite, quite audibly, "isn't that the nice young man you had in mind for yourself? Looks like you missed your chance, dearie."

Mortified, I fled back to the suite, leaving Rusty-Jean with the man of my dreams, and Mrs. Braithwaite, still stumping up and down the moonlit beach, crying at intervals, "Melvin, where are you?"

For the first time I found myself totally in sympathy with Mr. Braithwaite's apparent disinclination to answer her.

Unfortunately, the worst discovery of all was awaiting me when I reached the supposed sanctuary of my room. My third roommate, Spike, who has not spoken six words to any of us since we were assigned our quarters, and who I had assumed was merely shy, was lying sprawled on her bed, vividly illuminated in a shaft of moonlight, with her arms around a rather odd-looking woman from Detroit whom I'd met at lunch, with an extremely short upper lip!

Well, dear diary, as you can imagine, I hardly knew where to turn. Luckily, both were sound asleep (exhausted from what exertions, I shudder to speculate), and so I was able to snatch up you, trusty day-book, and a pen before tiptoeing out of the room.

Thanks to the full moon, it's actually quite light out here on the verandah, light enough to write by, and to make out the forms of numerous contented couples, strolling arm in arm along the beach in a way that, for some unaccountable reason, brings a slight lump to my throat.

Unfortunately, the mosquitoes are as much in evidence as the lovers, and are as big as Sopwith Camels – despite what the club brochure said about a complete absence of biting insects on the island. And farther down the beach I can discern the shape of what looks like a very large and hirsute spider making its way toward me, inexorably but without apparent haste.

I can only hope this unattractive creature is on its way over to assist with the mosquito problem, although I somehow doubt it.

What on earth are Tharma and Rusty-Jean going to say when they come home and learn what Spike is up to? *If* they come home, that is.

We are now three days on the island, and most of the talk centres around grumbling about the food (melon and rice, rice and melon) and about the overbearing ways of our social director, Mr. Krieg.

We are, all of us, appalled at how mercilessly he drives us to play endless tennis matches under a broiling sun, at what inane and embarrassing skits he subjects us to in the lounge after dinner, and at how insensitively he compels the shy girls to enter into the tasteless get-acquainted games. Embarrassment runs high amongst those who are forced to pass oranges under their chins to strange men, and to carry coconuts between their knees, depositing them into a bucket at the other end of the room. Had not Mr. Crispin and I emerged as the Grand Prize winners in the orange-pass playoffs, I know I should have been thoroughly mortified myself.

Mr. Crispin – whom I find myself liking more and more – barely tolerates Krieg. That much is plain to anyone with eyes, and what is plainer is how thoroughly Krieg shares the antipathy. God knows where this mutual aversion will lead. . . .

Meanwhile, I am overjoyed to have discovered in Mr. Crispin a fellow admirer of the writings of William Dean Howells, as well as a kindred enthusiast of ornithology. Having discovered these twin passions over a lunch of rice and melon, I attempted to drop over to the assistant social director's quarters to show him a particularly fine volume I have brought with me on tropical birds – none of which I've yet seen on the wing here on the island, where the only wildlife evident is insects.

However, Mr. Crispin's window blinds were drawn forbiddingly, and after my timid knock went unanswered, I withdrew, leaving the bird book on the step with a cordial note. Curiously, just as I was walking down the path, I thought I heard the sound of a woman's laughter emanating from Mr. Crispin's cabin, a laugh oddly reminiscent of Rusty-Jean's.

That, of course, simply cannot be, since a man of Mr. Crispin's breeding and background would never, I am convinced, so much as look at a vulgar creature like that. Besides which, Rusty-Jean seems utterly and wholly occupied with the ongoing seduction of the hapless young man formerly concussed, whose medical dressing has now shrunk down to an unobtrusive Band-Aid, and who can be seen trotting after her along the beach like a docile little dog. On closer inspection, he seems very weak-chinned, and not nearly as good-looking as I first imagined him to be.

Rusty-Jean never so much as comes near our room, not even to change her wristbands, which is a blessing, since with the woman from Detroit all but moved in, things have become a touch crowded. Naturally enough, I can't bring myself to spend the night under the same roof with the two lovebirds, so I have taken to sleeping on the verandah permanently now, with a rolled-up *Hot Rod* magazine at the ready to dispatch the mosquitoes, and one of the dinghy oars from the boat dock near by to deal with the spiders, who roam the beach by night in uncontrolled gangs.

Tharma is also often absent, although she seems to have cashiered the acne-sufferer in favor of the bald complaining gentleman I encountered in the drinks line-up the first day. Honestly, my heart goes out to desperate women like Tharma, Spike, and Rusty-Jean, forced by loneliness to consort with such riffraff.

Oh, I almost forgot to mention that Mrs. Braithwaite *still* hasn't located her husband, and is now beginning to make something of a nuisance of herself at mealtimes, demanding that whoever is unfortunate enough to be seated next to her help in her hunt, petitioning the club officials to strike a search-party, and similar overreactive measures.

The women unlucky enough to share accommodation with her, and I are jointly of the opinion that Mr. Braithwaite's disappearance is a judgment against her for the relentless, mindless cheerfulness she insisted upon inflicting on all of us early in our sojourn, but none of us has the heart to tell her so, of course.

Instead – when we deign to speak to her at all – we point out that, since all of her husband's belongings are intact in the room he lately shared with two other middle-aged gentlemen, it is highly unlikely that he can have wandered off very far.

Still, it remains unequivocally true that Mr. Braithwaite is nowhere to be seen. Ah well, just one of life's little mysteries, I suppose. And so to bed.

Four days since our arrival in this isolated place, and today events have begun to unfold themselves so dramatically that I confess myself almost too astounded to record them. Today, the murmurings against Mr. Krieg have escalated into a loud roar, as the various examples of his fanatical behavior have led many of us to believe, almost against our will, that the social director of the Ecstasy Island Beach Club – the person upon whom the happiness and well-being of so many utterly depend – may be mentally unbalanced.

But it was this morning's incident of the ping-pong balls that finally drove us to take action.

Although the day dawned hot and sunny as usual, Mr. Krieg without warning announced that we were all to repair to the games room for a round-robin tournament of table tennis. At this, many of the seasoned club guests were shocked and amazed. Not only is an indoor game played during optimum tanning hours entirely unheard of at a resort facility, some of the superstitious old veterans even expressed themselves of the opinion that such behavior at a club is downright unlucky.

But Krieg, his eyes bulging angrily and a fleck of foam gleaming at the corner of his lip, insisted that the game commence, leaving us and dear Mr. Crispin no choice but to follow him obediently, if reluctantly, to the games room.

Once there, however, Mr. Krieg made a startling discovery. Several brand-new ping-pong balls were apparently missing. Well! What a to-do Krieg made, counting and recounting the balls, demanding that all of us turn out our pockets like common thieves. Then, when his interrogations produced no results, he suddenly demanded that a measure of sand be brought up from the beach, as well as an ice-cream scoop from the kitchen.

"Now," declared Krieg, once the items were fetched, and as we all looked on, mystified, "let us say that this pile of sand represents the total number of ping-pong balls – "

At that point, Mr. Crispin made a choking sound, as if stifling laughter, and Krieg wheeled on him sharply. "Yes, Mr. Crispin? You have something to say?"

"Look, this is kind of ridiculous, isn't it?" spoke up Crispin stoutly. "I mean, who cares how many ping-pong balls – "

"I care, Mr. Crispin, and so should you!" And having so said, Krieg began scooping up sand. "Now, we know that four ping-pong balls were stepped on, so I take away four scoops of sand – "

At this, Mr. Crispin could endure no more. "All right, Krieg, all right. *I* took the damn ping-pong balls. There! Are you satisfied?"

The social director's face went the color of very good claret – the sort of claret that has never been served here at the club. "You? And may I ask why you took them, Mr. Crispin?"

"Because I can't take any more of your tyranny!" Crispin declared passionately. "And I'm not the only one. Come on, speak up, you people. . . . " As he appealed to us with a look, I realized as if for the first time how truly magnificent he is. "Tell him that you're exhausted from compulsory water-skiing, sick of non-stop disco. And tired – so bloody tired – of his endless get-acquainted games!"

Well. Dear diary, what can I say? The consequences of Mr. Crispin's rash outburst proved serious indeed. Still flushing violently purple, Krieg ordered all guests to the shuffleboard court, to witness punishment. Duly we all hurried along behind Mr. Krieg and Mr. Crispin to the court, and as we did so, I confess that my heart went out to Mr. Crispin, whose manly defiance of Krieg was about to cost him so much.

Sure enough, when we reached the court, Krieg turned to us all with triumphant relish, to announce the extent of his harsh discipline: Mr. Crispin was ordered to play six games of shuffleboard with old Mrs. Trumbo!

All of us gasped at such barbarity, and even the staunch Mr. Crispin looked as though his nerve had failed him a little. Six games, with old deaf Mrs. Trumbo, who continually forgets which color she is playing, and demands to hear the score once every fourteen seconds.

"One!" called out Krieg pitilessly, to indicate that the first game should begin.

As Mr. Crispin bit his lip in anticipation of the pain to come, removed his shirt to display a very handsome physique indeed, and prepared himself for his ordeal, righteous indignation began to kindle in the bosom of each of us bystanders. Mutterings of "Shocking" and "Unfair" could be heard intermingled with the sharp thwack! of the shuffleboard discs.

"Two!" barked Krieg. Thwack! "Three!" Thwack! Thwack! "Four!"

By now, beads of perspiration stood out on Mr. Crispin's brow and we marvelled that he did not cry out. But still more marvellous was the total absence of evidence of pity from Krieg for his poor assistant's ordeal. And when the end of the sixth game was finally reached, and a sweating Mr. Crispin threw down his stick, exclaiming "There! I hope you're satisfied!", Krieg turned on him with a demented snarl to say, "You're not finished yet, Crispin. Go on to seven."

Seven! This final outrage was too much for all of us. As one, we rose against the social director, and with the help of Mr. Crispin – who suddenly seemed to have regained his strength – we dragged Krieg, kicking and protesting vehemently, down to the beach.

Many in the group (myself included) were all for throwing him bodily into the sea, but Mr. Crispin – that benevolent angel among men – intervened, and in the end it was his sanity that prevailed to save Krieg's life.

"No!" he declared. "I'm in charge now, and I say he will not be drowned. Set him adrift on that air mattress, with a shakerful of daiquiris, some guacamole dip, and enough nachos to see him to the nearest port. I'm the social director of this club now."

Well, dear diary, to try to compress a long story at least somewhat, we did as Mr. Crispin ordered, and shoved our social director, along with the few guests who'd remained loyal to him, out to the sea on an air mattress.

"I'll see you paid for this, Crispin!" Krieg vowed angrily as his mattress bobbed farther and farther out from shore. "If I ever see the Resort Directors Association office again, I swear you'll be paid for this."

At these dire imprecations, I will admit, a shudder ran through me, and my sudden impulse was to run to Mr. Crispin and to fling myself protectively against him, like a shield between Krieg's harsh words and Crispin's tender heart.

Halfway to him, however, better sense was restored to me, and I settled for grasping his hand and impulsively inviting myself to his quarters to read aloud to him from the works of William Dean Howells that I had brought with me to the island.

Mr. Crispin seemed, for some reason, distracted, and for a moment he did not appear to attend to what I was saying. At last, though, he got the point, but he must still have been in a state of bedazzlement from his sudden elevation to the rank of social director, because all he said to me was, "Look, some other time, okay?"

Such a marvellous man, born to command. I shall dedicate the rest of my holiday to satisfying his every whim. My mind is made up to it. And hang the consequences.

It is now two days since the mutiny against Krieg, and it is with a heavy heart that I pick up my pen to report on the disturbing events that have occurred in the intervening time.

My roommate Spike and the woman from Detroit have had a terrible falling-out, with the result that everything is over between them, and now Spike is casting such looks of longing at *me* that I have elected to continue sleeping out on the verandah, and have stepped up my armaments to *two* dinghy oars.

Since yesterday, when Mr. Braithwaite came out from underneath the boat dock where he's been hiding all this time, Mrs. Braithwaite runs the gamut of emotions, alternately overjoyed and furious – because, as it turns out, Mr. Braithwaite was hiding under the boat dock with Rusty-Jean, who has apparently been gratifying his every physical craving, in the very few free moments she manages to find between her other lurid assignations.

But far more startling than that – imagine my disgust and revulsion, dear inanimate confidant, when I dropped in last night on Mr. Crispin unannounced to find the ubiquitous Rusty-Jean lounging on his bed, a foot propped up on the handsome ornithological volume I had previously lent to Crispin, as she applied a vivid nail-varnish to her toes and peered through the interference at a rerun of *Adam-12* on the television set.

How disappointed I am with Mr. Crispin, dear diary, only you, recipient of my private-most thoughts, will readily understand. For one thing, there are supposed to be no television sets on the island. For another, when Mr. Crispin came into the room in response to my exclamation of surprise at seeing Rusty-Jean, he was towelling off from the shower, to which he'd obviously repaired to wash away evidence of his lust, and he seemed not in the slightest degree glad to see me. Nor did he make any attempt at an apology, or at an explanation of Rusty-Jean's presence, or any excuse for the streaks of nail-polish on the cover of my book.

"Look, lady," was all he said, "if it's about the scheduled hike to the Hanging Rock, forget it. No way I'm taking that on tomorrow, with all I have to do. Get yourself a map at the Hospitality Desk and find the road yourself."

The look of freezing scorn I gave him on my way out of his room is something Crispin is not soon likely to forget.

In addition to all the private woes in the club, and perhaps harsher than any individual sorrow (with the possible exception of mine), is the great general unhappiness that has arisen amongst the guests, in the face of Mr. Crispin's lackadaisical and inadequate stewardship.

For, sad to tell, conditions on Ecstasy Island are now much worse than ever they were under Mr. Krieg. Not only is the melon-and-rice diet as unvarying as before, but Mr. Crispin – though an able enough organizer of charades – is no hand at all at skit-writing, and has proven himself utterly incapable of choosing themes for the nightly dances. Two nights running now, we have had a Country Hoedown.

Moreover, now that Krieg is gone, it seems that many are actually nostalgic for his exhausting regime of fun-fun-fun. Besotted with his doxy, Crispin pays no attention to the social needs of the single people in our midst, and I myself am one of those who readily admits to missing those get-acquainted sessions of passing oranges and dropping coconuts into the bucket. And what many of us would not give for a few sets of compulsory tennis under a wilting tropical sun!

Yes, Mr. Crispin is a changed man, and not at all as I first judged him. Sullen, moody, aloof, he cannot even remember to keep the bar stocks replenished. Last night saw the last of the stuffed olives, and rumor has it we are running dangerously low on Clamato juice. . . .

Today I have hardly strength to write at all. Word has it the bus will come tomorrow to take us back to the airport and thence home. There are few of us left who believe that, however.

All the ping-pong balls are gone now, but Crispin seems not to care, and only laughs wildly, mockingly, when the matter is brought to his attention. Many have taken to their beds, weak from lack of competitive sport. Still others, no shells left to purchase food or drink, go hungry. And before last night's dance, when Crispin told us the theme for that night would again be a Country Hoedown, there were those who sneered openly in his face.

Robbed of nourishment, of physical activity, and of social life, the guests turn more and more upon themselves – and upon each other. Mrs. Braithwaite now keeps her husband tied to the handle of her suitcase with a length of elasticized cord, a circumstance which has so demoralized Mr. Braithwaite that only this morning, I distinctly saw him snap at a fly – and miss.

Rusty-Jean, the young man with the concussion (I never got a chance even to find out his name), and Crispin all go about together now, open in their indiscriminate affections. Why was it I had never noticed that trace of effeminacy in Mr. Crispin's walk before today?

Tharma has deserted the balding gentleman in favor of several of the kitchen help, and rumor has it that the fellow with acne lost his way to the Hanging Rock, thanks to the map from the Hospitality Desk, which turned out to be of Tulsa and Surrounding Area.

I'm glad that Spike and I have come to an understanding and have agreed upon a June wedding. That unexpected development, plus the discovery that the mosquitoes, left unmolested, will sting the spiders to death, are the only positive things to have come out of this trip.

Again and again the same haunting questions run through our minds: were we wrong to banish Krieg from our midst? Did Crispin manoeuvre us into doing it? Will God punish us by routing our return flight through Bonners Ferry, Idaho, and Aklavik? How can we stop from peeling, and will the peeled parts tan?

I don't know the answers. I doubt if any of us does. Meanwhile, we float aimlessly on our air mattresses, lost and derelict as so many ghost ships.

Oh, what I would not give now for a martini with a really large olive! Or a spirited skit in which the social director humorously imitates old Mrs. Trumbo windsurfing. Or even a dance organized around a Star Wars theme. . . .

God have pity on this wretched Beach Club, and every accursed soul in it. For I fear none of us will survive, even to see history's judgment levelled upon our mutiny. And even if some of us do manage to contrive to see home again, I know in my heart that our luggage will not come back with us.

May God have mercy upon us all. . . .

MANGIAMANIA

It happened when I called up a friend to find out about her first date with a new man the night before.

"So how was it?"

"Terrific. We went to that new restaurant, the Italian place."

"Sounds romantic."

"No, Northern Italian, actually. The cuisine of Rome is spicier. This place has white sauces to die for and – "

"Wait a sec. What about your date?"

"Oh, he started with the *zuppa del giorno*, then moved on to – "

"No, what I'm asking is: How did the evening go?"

"Not bad. Sixty bucks for two, including wine and tip."

Click.

As I hung up the receiver, I suddenly recalled how my friend had met this new man. Over a tray of green peppercorns in a gourmet food shop. Somehow, it seemed significant.

And what also seemed significant, now that I thought about it, was the means by which three of my other friends had recently met *their* new guys. One in a cooking course titled "French Without Fear". Another while browsing through a copy of *Gourmet* magazine in a bookstore. And the third, reaching for the same package of *linguine verde* on the grocery shelf.

Click. Click. Click.

Yes, something was definitely happening here. I decided that a walk downtown would help me sort it all out.

Food, I realized, as I passed the fourth store window in a row proclaiming a sale on wine thermometers and lettuce driers, had completely taken over. The kind of enthusiasm people used to pour into collecting stamps and breeding chinchillas was now being squandered on *crème anglaise* and red lettuce. And that wasn't all. As I stopped for a moment outside a love shop, where the red satin lips dangling in the window had a "Going Out of Business" sign pinned to them, the full horror of the situation dawned on me. The sensual thrill of erotica had been all but eclipsed by the new mangiamania.

Well, damn it all, I thought. The old libidinous order can't be allowed to just pass away. Not while there's breath in this oh-so-willing body. I squared my shoulders and, turning my back forever on lettuce driers, marched bravely into the love shop.

L'Amour français was the promising title of the video cassette I selected and carried home with me in the deepening dusk.

Ah, what a treat. Curled up in bed with a lushly smutty movie, devouring lustful images more eagerly than champagne truffles from Fauchon...

The film opened with a pouty young French man picking up a pouty young French girl on a wharf in Marseilles. Exactly *how* he picked her up, however, I failed to notice, because for some reason my interest was caught by all the fish strewn on the pier. I could just imagine them pan-fried with a soupçon of butter, and some freshly crushed garlic.

By the time I pulled myself back to the story line, the pouty French couple (I didn't catch their names, I was too busy watching them nibble flaky croissants from a *pâtisserie*) were back at his place, feverishly removing their clothes.

At that point, things got pretty hot and heavy – at least, I imagine they did. Unfortunately, my attention had been totally captivated by a still-life painting over their bed, featuring a neatly peeled Seville orange, some Anjou pears, a pomegranate (out of season), and a loaf of crusty bread, sprinkled with –

Click.

Trembling and furious with myself, I snapped off the set. What on earth was happening to me?

Frantic now, I rummaged in my dresser drawer for a novel I'd picked up in the drugstore a day or two before. Ah, here it was. *First Blissful Encounter*. Now, surely a chapter or two of that was all

I needed to reaffirm that what I was looking for was the food of love, not vice versa.

Trying to feel confident, I opened the book on the first page. "It all began," I read, "with a kiss from my companion." Now that, I thought, was a very routine way for an evening to begin. And did they *both* have to start with the kiss? Couldn't her companion have ordered something different?

"At first," the book went on, "his caresses seemed bland." Yes, I could imagine the kind of bland caresses her companion would serve up, seasoned without inspiration. Fondly I cast my mind back to some truly outstanding kisses I had read about, kisses of the delectable sort available in the great European capitals, where the men not only make them spicy, but also totally fresh.

"At last, he took me in his arms, tenderly, delicately." Good grief, I scoffed, you call *that* a hug? A hug should always be robust and full-bodied, and heated to such a temperature that it can completely melt any resistance that –

Oh my God. I slammed shut the covers of the book, the cold sweat pouring down my neck. Could it be that mangiamania had claimed another victim?

Striving to be calm, I padded out to the kitchen to see what I could find in the fridge. I don't know why, but I always think better with something to eat. A wedge of perfectly aged Gorgonzola, accompanied by fragrant muscat grapes, and perhaps a chilled glass of that incomparable Bordeaux that everyone is...

The Big Game
Explained

Contrary to the impression sportscasters like to give, not everybody in this country looks forward to the Grey Cup game.

There are, in fact, enormous gangs of you out there to whom the Cup, the teams who vie for it, and indeed the hallowed sport of football itself (hereinafter referred to as The Game), mean nothing at all.

Fortunately, I am not one of them. I adore the Grey Cup, and exist for that November weekend on which it is competed for. That's because I have the distinct advantage of being knowledgeable about The Game in general, and about the Grey Cup game (hereinafter referred to as The Big Game) in particular.

Furthermore, it's my determined belief that any of you who understand The Game will become interested in it, and any of you who take the trouble to familiarize yourselves with the history and psychology of The Big Game cannot fail to turn into devoted fans, faster than you can say Frank Tripuka.

So, let's begin our crash course on The Game and The Big Game with a quick look backward to Where It All Began.

Where it all began, naturally enough, was in the States. And that's pretty much where it has stayed. The best players of The Game are still Americans, and the less talented among them still regularly move up to Canada to help us out with our version of The Game, which we've managed to keep distinctly Canadian by adding a man (Canadians never see any harm in hiring on extra personnel), reducing the number of downs (Canadians never see any harm in making things harder), and altering the size of the field (for the same reason that we have a two-dollar bill; in this country, it's the *illusion* of autonomy that counts).

Way back when, however, when a team from McGill University went down to play The First Game against Harvard, Canadians had no reason to suspect that we were not going to be equal participants in the creation of The Game.

As far as I know, no clear records of that first scrimmage are extant, but I bet I can make a few shrewd assumptions as to how the day went.

First of all, there's no question in my mind that Harvard had the better-looking cheerleaders, not to mention a classier half-time show. No doubt the Harvard players were also paid much better, and could augment their incomes through lucrative product endorsements. While the poor McGill players found themselves with nothing more tempting than requests from the Heart Fund to do free commercials, and the opportunity to appear on talk shows in Chicoutimi.

As if all that weren't humiliating enough, I can just imagine what it was like out there on the field for the Canadians, in a game where the rules were presumably being made up as things went along.

I'll bet you anything that tackling was introduced by the Americans, and probably in the most unceremonious way. While the McGill team was still discussing how to decide to form a committee to investigate various methods of player interception, the boisterous Yanks probably just jumped them, thereby forcing a point of view upon their gentle Northern neighbors.

As for the ball itself, doubtless McGill brought a live pig with them, which was slaughtered, tanned, stitched, and stuffed by American labor, then sold back to the Canadians at the end of the game at an exorbitant mark-up.

But in spite of its inauspicious beginning, The Game has taken feverish hold in this country, and nowhere is this more evident than in an examination of The Big Game, and of the cup for which it is named.

The Grey Cup (more properly referred to in these metric times as the Grey Quarter-Litre) is quintessentially Canadian, as a close analysis of its name reveals. First, the significance of the fact that it is a cup. The Americans – a more lavish people generally – measure their football in bowls. And they take care that it's always a bowl of *something* – roses, oranges, cotton; even 'gators will do in a pinch.

What have we got? A cup full of grey. A color evocative only of dirty snowbanks, slightly soiled flannel jackets marked down at The Bay, and mid-winter Canadian skin tones. Ugh.

But despite the uninspiring nature of the trophy, The Big Game is an important cultural event, and there's absolutely no reason you should let yourself be left out, simply because some of the traditions attendant upon it make no sense to you.

To better your understanding, I've prepared a Quick Checklist of some of the most common questions asked about The Big Game.

QUESTION ONE: If The Game is a popular pastime all across this great land of ours, how come no teams from the Maritimes ever compete in The Big Game?

ANSWER: For the same reason there are no Maritime hockey or baseball franchises. The names Nova Scotia, New Brunswick, and Prince Edward Island are simply too long to be printed neatly across the back of a uniform.

QUESTION TWO: How come you didn't say anything about Newfoundland?

ANSWER: All right, if you insist. How many Newfoundlanders does it take to make up a football team?

QUESTION THREE: I don't know. How many?

ANSWER: Twelve. Ten to hold them down, and two to apply the makeup.

QUESTION FOUR: How on earth did you come up with a joke as terrible as that?

ANSWER: Oh shut up. Anyway, you're supposed to be asking me questions about football.

QUESTION FIVE: Why is it that The Big Game's location is continually shifted from East to West and back again?

ANSWER: Because that's how a sense of tension is provided. Every year we get to wonder if it's going to rain during The Big Game (Vancouver), or will it snow (Toronto)?

QUESTION SIX: But doesn't Vancouver now have a domed stadium?

ANSWER: Hey, you're brighter than you've been letting on. You're right, Vancouver does have a dome, so now we have to focus our tension on whether it's going to rain or snow on The Big Parade preceding The Big Game. Of course, if Toronto ever gets its domed stadium, the distinction between the two cities will keel over on the astroturf faster than you can say Sam Etcheverry. The only distinguishing feature then will be that in Toronto people say, "Have a nice day, eh?" while in Vancouver they say, "Hey, have a nice day."

QUESTION SEVEN: Why is it that –

ANSWER: I'm sorry, that's all the time we have for questions. Time to move on to a Short Glossary to explain some of the more puzzling terms associated with The Big Game.

Short Glossary of Big Game Terms

TIGHT END – The way the players look in those funny pants during The Big Game.

DEFENSIVE END – The explanations the players offer for why they have to wear those funny pants during The Big Game.

QUARTERBACK SNEAK – When one of the TV viewers of The Big Game surreptitiously removes twenty-five cents from the pile of money everyone has chipped in for pizza.

HANDKERCHIEF ON THE PLAY – Phenomenon of lachrymose wives who wanted to watch Shakespeare on PBS, but their husbands insisted on seeing The Big Game instead.

SACKING THE QUARTERBACK – When the person who surreptitiously removed twenty-five cents from the pizza-money pile surreptitiously slips the coin into a bag while everyone else is caught up in watching The Big Game.

Now that your most pressing questions have been answered, and the more puzzling terminology has been elucidated, you're ready to join the rabid thousands to whom The Big Game embodies a quality of meaningfulness otherwise absent from their lives.

Just make sure nobody suckers you into playing a game of *electronic* football during half-time. Electronic football (in whose evolutionary history Canadians played no part whatsoever) is a whole other story, which you must remind me to tell you about some time.

In fact, if you're very good, quicker than you can say Cookie Gilchrist, my guide to electronic football (hereinafter referred to as The Little Game) will become available in a bookstore near you.

Awake and Single

The news that our friend Sarah (a.k.a. Swinging Sally) had decided to get married ran through the single community like a shock wave; it clanged into our joint consciousness like a discordant death knell; it breathed down our collective neck like a cold cold wind.

Sarah? Our Sarah, of all people, tying the proverbial knot? Rushing headlong into the abyss, crossing over into that undiscovered country from whose bourn no traveller returns?

Sarah had always been such a good-time girl, such a quintessentially carefree single, that she was, quite literally, the last person on earth we would have taken for the marrying kind. And we all tried to tell her so, that night in the bar.

"Sarah," we said, "you're the last person on earth we – "

"Hold it," said Sarah. "Just stop right there. I know what you're going to say, and I don't want to hear it."

The rest of us exchanged quizzical looks. Was it our imagination, or was Sarah sounding a mite defensive?

"Look," persisted Rosalie, undeterred. (Rosalie was seldom deterred, which was, we all generally agreed, the major problem with Rosalie. Although it did appear that, in this particular instance, her legendary undeterrability might actually come in handy.) "Look, as far as I can see, you don't even *like* Elmer. You're forever complaining about the way he reads the movie credits out loud, and keeps his money stapled to his undershirt."

"That's right," Maribeth added. "And what about the weird expression he gets on his face whenever he chops up mice for his boa? You want to live with that every day of your life?"

"It won't be every day," Sarah pointed out. "The boa only eats once a month. Anyway, so what if Elmer is hardly my beau ideal – "

"Your boa ideal?"

"Ha ha. The point is, Elmer's a damn sight better than Raymond was. Or Delbert...or Ernie, for that matter. Remember eerie Ernie? And his hairnet?"

"Yes," I said shortly. I certainly did remember Ernie, since I'd been dating him myself for the past six months. It seemed unnecessarily cruel of Sarah to bring up the business of the hairnet, particularly in front of everyone. Plainly, our barrage of questions about her marital plans had nettled her into retaliatory action.

"Nevertheless," said Maribeth, "that doesn't mean you have to give up the search and settle for Elmer. You're young, Sarah – just like the rest of us. And there are plenty more fish in the – "

"That's exactly the problem," Sarah interrupted. "Plenty of fish. When what we're looking for is men."

At this point Cilla, who'd so far made no comment, spoke up. "Still and all, no law says you have to rush to the altar with Elmer, even if nothing better ever does come along. The single life is terrific, Sarah. There's no life like it."

"I thought that was the Armed Forces."

"Hey, maybe *that's* what we should do," said Maribeth. "Join the army. Meet some real men for a change."

"Oh sure. Real men. An eighteen-year-old turret-gunner with an *Action Comics* collection is your idea of a real man, I suppose?"

"Come on, the way I hear it, many of those Armed Forces guys are as old as twenty-six, and sometimes their skin conditions are even operable."

"Anyway," Cilla continued, while the rest of us giggled shrilly, "men or no men, being single is definitely one of the great bargains of our time. I mean, think about it. Here we all are, at ten o'clock on a week night, free to sit chatting together in the bar, enjoying each other's company.... You think married people can get away with that? If any of us were living with anybody else right

now, we'd be rushing to the phone, calling home for permission to
stay out another half-hour – "

"Or checking with the sitter," I put in, "to see whether, for
another thirty bucks, she'd let me get her home a minute after
twelve."

"Or coping with a weeping kid on the other end of the line,
trying to explain that Mommy's entitled to a night out once in a
while."

"That reminds me," said Rosalie, rummaging in her change
purse. "I should call Wally."

"Rosalie," said Sarah, "Wally is a Scotch terrier – "

"Lakeland. He's a Lakeland terrier."

"Well, whatever. He doesn't know how to answer the phone."

A quarter gripped in her hand, Rosalie pushed back her chair
and got up. "He recognizes my ring. It lets him know Mamma will
be home within the hour."

Sarah shook her head in disgust as we all watched Rosalie
thread her way through the bar over to the bank of phones. "No
life like it, huh? Sure, it's great to be single all right. Just ask
Rosalie. No, better yet ask Wally."

"Rosalie is an exceptional case," Maribeth argued. "Most of the
rest of us wear our singledom with dignity, like a diamond tiara.
Especially you, Sarah. You're about the classiest single woman I
know."

"Thanks," Sarah smiled, her defensiveness melting, as Maribeth had known it would. "But my mind's made up. Come next
Saturday, Elmer, the boa, and I are tying the knot. I can't remain
the member of an oppressed minority forever."

Oppressed? Us? What on earth was she talking about? Although·
we were bursting with curiosity, it seemed too important a revela-
tion to exclude Rosalie, so we all very considerately waited for her
to return from calling Wally before pressing Sarah to explain what
she meant by "oppressed minority".

"It came to me the other night in a blinding flash," she told us.
"It was late, I couldn't sleep . . . You know, the usual."

As one, we all nodded. Boy, did we know. Being single was
terrific in broad daylight. During the evening hours it was generally quite tolerable. But in the middle of the night, especially when

waking up to a noise that sounded exactly like the noise a mad rapist would make if he'd elected to make his entrance through the letter slot, wearing aluminum siding and dragging a bowling-ball attached to a bicycle chain? No fun. No fun at all.

"This time, it wasn't a sound or anything that woke me up," Sarah hastened to assure us. "It was just this...realization. A realization that in the past week alone, I'd received urgent pleas through the mail from two gay-rights groups, one senior citizens' lobby, four deprived racial minorities, three feminist outfits, and six kinds of political refugee. But not one brochure from any organization claiming to represent singles, the most oppressed minority group of them all."

"Come on," said Cilla. "We don't have it all that bad." She swallowed, licking her lips nervously. "Do we?"

"Think about it," Sarah advised. "That's what I did, lying there in my narrow cot, awake and single at four a.m. I thought, first of all, about how much we have to pay for the privilege of being unencumbered and unattached.

"Like no tax breaks for singles, no family allowance – okay, fine, I don't like that, but I can live with it. What really gets my goat, though, is going on a package holiday to the Caribbean, and having to pay a 'single supplement'. As though arriving at a resort without a mate were some careless oversight on my part that has to be penalized."

"It's true. And then there are all those on-site expenses a single incurs on vacation. The overweight suitcase you had to pay extra for because you can't afford to show up with fewer than nine wardrobe changes per vacation day," Rosalie sighed.

"And not just any old wardrobe," I agreed. "An expensive designer ensemble that's going to set you head and shoulders above those six hundred other single women who've arrived on the island in the same tour group, to compete for the attentions of seven short, bald accountants."

"Not to mention more suntan lotion, costlier emollients, a better class of perfume, and flashier jewellery than married women are required to shell out for. Married women get to schlepp around the beach in a Pablum-stained muumuu, rubber thongs, a layer of Noskote, and a third-degree sunburn. What do they care how they look on vacation? No matter what, they know they're going home with the same person they arrived with."

By now, we sounded like a woeful Greek chorus, strophing and antistrophing our various grievances to razor sharpness, as we stabbed desultorily at the wilted lemon slices lying at the bottom of our glasses with the green plastic cocktail sticks that read "Whoopee" in raised letters.

"You see?" Sarah signalled the waiter to bring another round of spritzers. "The more you think about it, the worse it gets. And that's just the holiday picture. Things are even bleaker once you get back home. For one thing, food products always come packaged with the Kettle family in mind. Single people wind up buying everything in such huge amounts that it's broccoli every night for a week, just to use the damn stuff up before it wilts, and four hundred and eighty-seven ways to prepare puffed wheat."

"Pickles," declared Rosalie. "They're the worst. My God, selecting a fur coat is a trivial decision compared to purchasing jars that are so enormous that you're looking at a year's commitment, minimum, to whether it's going to be dill or bread-and-butter."

"You know what gets my vote? Spices. I mean, how much cream of tartar is one person expected to use in a lifetime? If they don't put it in smaller tins, I'm going to have to start buying the stuff on a time-share basis with six other singles. And do you realize that there are seven million, four hundred thirty-six thousand, and forty-four pinches of cayenne in the average container? I could cater all of Mexico with that."

"Of course, there is a solution," said Sarah ominously. "The only other solution – besides matrimony – that society has managed to come up with to date."

"Boil-in-the-bag dinners!" we chorused despairingly. "Never! Anything but boil-in-the-bag dinners. Tiny little helpings of turkey tetrazzini, with two peas, half a button mushroom, and an eyedropperful of cream sauce. Fettuccine alfredo made from a single noodle, and Oriental Surprise – where the only surprise is how deceptively large they can package one chunk of pineapple and six grains of rice."

"Let's face it," I said. "They've really got us singles where they want us. And not only is there a fortune to be made from the overpriced crud we're forced to buy for ourselves, what about the flourishing industry that's grown up around producing useless gimcracks for other people to buy for us?"

"Pet accessories – every single woman I know with a cat or budgie gets bombarded with them. Do you have any idea how many little plaster castles friends have bought over the years for my goldfish, Parsifal? How many plaster treasure chests, and plaster deep-sea divers? Poor Parsifal. Eventually his bowl got so overrun with architecture that the city reclassified it as a commercial zone. Now Parsifal has no idea how he's going to pay the taxes."

"My Wally has seventeen rubber fire hydrants, eleven wool plaid coats, and eight sets of plastic rain booties," Rosalie reported. Then she giggled. "Of course, those are just the prezzies I've bought him myself over the years."

"And what about that set of the *Encyclopaedia Britannica*?" Cilla reminded her. "Plus you got him his own video cassette of *Old Yeller*. As well as a hair drier, a gift set of Brut, and a sterling silver water dish with his name engraved on it."

"You know, I don't mind so much when people feel they're obliged to get a Christmas present for my cat, just because I'm too immature and pathetically disorganized to have gotten married and had children instead. What rots my socks, though, is when married friends insist on giving me a house plant for my birthday, just so I'll have 'something to love'. Love a rubber plant? Ick. Is that even legal in this province, I wonder?"

"Okay," said Sarah, "you all see what I'm talking about. Being a single is no ride on the Ferris wheel, right? So can't you understand why, after tossing and turning for several sleepless hours, I would make my mind up just to pack the whole thing in?"

"No," Rosalie replied with spirit. "I do not. When conditions are unjust, you don't just give in. You fight."

"You know, Rosalie's right. Singles are indispensable. The rest of the world can't get along without us, and secretly they know it."

Sarah pulled a face. "Come on, you can't fight City Hall, haven't you heard? Particularly the wedding licence bureau."

Maribeth sucked the rest of her spritzer through the straw with noisy energy. "I agree with Rosalie and Cilla, absolutely. There are all kinds of contributions that singles make to society that none of the coupled world could get by without."

"For instance?" Sarah wanted to know.

"For instance, if there were no singles, who'd occupy the third seat in the row on airplanes? And who else could couples invite over to dinner on twenty minutes' notice?"

"Absolutely," I said. "And without single people, there'd be nobody willing to ride in the jump seat of sports cars."

"Nobody to leave the dog with when you go on holiday. Nobody around to buy ten-inch TV sets and two-cup teapots."

"If singles didn't exist, who'd rent basement apartments?"

"Who else would be sucker enough to buy those chocolate bars kids sell door-to-door to raise money for the school band?"

"Single people are the only people able to stay awake for the ending of the Late Late Show. Otherwise, how would couples ever find out how the movie came out?" Cilla pointed out.

"Most important of all," declared Sarah, obviously caught up in the spirit of the thing, "without singles, who would married people fantasize leaving their spouses for?"

Flushed and ecstatic, we all brought our spritzer glasses together, in a spontaneous toast to the glory of singledom, forever and aye.

Suddenly realizing what she was endorsing, Sarah withdrew her goblet from the general salutation and looked abruptly away. "Look," she said through tight lips, "I know what you're trying to do, and it's no use."

"Whatever are you talking about?" Maribeth inquired innocently.

"It's just no use," Sarah repeated. "I'm getting married Saturday, and there's no point arguing about it."

"Who's arguing?" demanded Rosalie. "Wally and I will be at the church, with bells on. In fact, if you're looking for someone to give the bride away – "

"No, Rosalie. Absolutely not. I am not going to be given away at my own wedding by an Airedale. Not even an Airedale with his own set of encyclopedias."

"He's not an Airedale; he's a Lakeland. Anyway, who are you going to get to give you away, if – "

"Give me away. Listen to this. It sounds like something out of the Middle Ages. I'm thirty-six years old, for God's sake. Do you think I have to be given away, like a place setting of chinaware or something, free with any purchase of a ball and chain?"

"Oh, Sarah, Sarah," sobbed Maribeth, overcome. "Don't do it. Please. Not yet. You're too good for Elmer. Wait for something better to come along."

"Honest to Christ," Sarah grumbled good-naturedly as we paid the tab, dickered over a tip, and, escorting the weeping Maribeth, prepared to depart. "You tell your best friends you've decided it's time to get married and where does it get you? Into the last reel of *Uncle Tom's Cabin*, with everybody swaying and keening over the body of Little Eva."

"I bet she's not going to do it!" Cilla announced suddenly, her eyes narrowed at Sarah in a shrewdly evaluative way. "It's true, isn't it, Sal? You've changed your mind, and decided to live to fight the good fight another day."

"G'wan." Sarah waved her arms at us in a mock gesture of dismissal as we all headed into the street, preparatory to fanning out in our separate directions to our separate cars. "I've never heard such a bunch of sentimental horse-doody. Get the hell home, all of you, and I'll see you on Saturday, at the gibbet."

"Keeps his money stapled to his undershirt," I whispered as I gave Sarah a farewell buss on the cheek. "Don't do it."

"Reads the movie credits aloud. Sarah, it won't be the same out here in Singleland without you," hissed Rosalie.

Exasperated, Sarah shooed us all away, and none of us spoke to her or saw her for the rest of the week.

That Saturday, however, we were all on hand to look on as Sarah, dry-eyed and composed, exchanged her vows with Elmer.

Shortly after the honeymoon, the invitations began. Sarah invited each of us, in succession, to dinner on less than an hour's notice. Sarah asked us, in turn, if we'd mind very much riding in the jump seat of Elmer's two-seater. At Christmastime, Sarah, who was by then pregnant, produced thoughtful presents for each of our pets, and a house plant for petless me, with a card attached saying "Something to love".

Before we knew it, Sarah was calling us up one by one to find out the ending of the Saturday night Late Late Show. To our credit, to our individual and everlasting credit, each of us would obligingly tell her how the movie had come out.

And not once did any of us, her very best friends, ever say, "I told you so."

Invasion

of

the

Airline

Stewardesses

Like a lot of people for whom the ability to remain in constant motion functions as a life-saving device – much like protective coloring in some animals – I take a lot of airplanes. And in the course of my travels I run into more than my share of stewardesses.

Not stewardesses. Excuse me. Flight attendants. "Flight attendant" is that kind of meaningless adjective-noun airline phrase ("smoking materials" being the quintessential example) that has been designed by commercial airlines for maximum ambiguity (read: minimum legal liability) aboard regularly scheduled flights.

I've learned a lot about modern communication from studying the language of commercial aviation – almost as much, in fact, as I've learned about food from studying puréed carrots. And I'm here to share with you what I've managed to pick up.

Actually, the most instructive language-learning session I've ever had at a cruising altitude of 37,000 feet came to me on one journey when I was dozing off, into that never-never world between meditation and deep coma, shortly after the termination of the meal service and prior to the commencement of the inflight entertainment. . . .

Aw heck. No point in mincing words. You know the state I'm talking about. When you're completely ripped on the carafe of complimentary wine, too buzzed on chemically reconstituted chicken divan and apple charlotte to tune in to the flick, and consequently good for nothing but a sort of rapt and open-mouthed trance. Mine was that kind of haunting airborne dream that comes to you at such a moment.

In the dream, I had donned my complimentary headset specially designed to enhance my listening pleasure and had obediently tuned my armchair console (conveniently located within easy reach) to Channel Two, upon which movie reception was rumored to be about to commence in just a few moments' time.

Sure enough. Up came the ominous throb of the introductory chord; up came the opening title upon the viewing screen. *Invasion of the Airline Stewardesses!* was how the hysterical message read.

There was another suspenseful chord, then a tracking shot of a friendly middle-American midsummer street, followed by a sequence in which a young friendly middle-American midsummer man strode up the front walk of one of the middle-American houses to ring the doorbell in an open-hearted and purposeful way.

The door opened, and a young woman with a fringe of dark hair appeared, looking out with an expectant smile.

"Hi there, Mary Lou," said the young man. "Ready for our picnic?"

Whereupon the young woman opened the door wider and ushered him in, her smile decidedly mechanical now. "Good afternoon, Steve. Welcome to Number Seven-Forty-Seven Boeing Street. Our house temperature today is maintained at a moderate seventy-two degrees Fahren – "

"Pardon?" said Steve, with an uneasy grin.

"However," Mary Lou continued, "should you at any time during your visit today become uncomfortable, you will find a thermostat located within easy reach in the front hallway."

"Mary Lou," said Steve, kindly but firmly, "I'm here to take you to Lake Periphrastic for a picnic, remember?"

But Mary Lou appeared to take no notice as she led him to an armchair in the living room, plumping up the pillow before indicating he should sit. "For your added visiting pleasure a beverage service is available to you this afternoon. Should you – "

"Mary Lou!" Steve was snapping at her now. "Cut it out! It's Steve, your fiancé. Don't you know me?"

"Because of the short duration of your visit this afternoon, there will be no hot-meal service available."

His face ashen, Steve rose out of the armchair with an expression of unalloyed alarm. "Mary Lou, what in the consarned heck's happened to you?"

"Our visiting time this afternoon will be approximately – "

At that point, Steve cut her off. "Stay right where you are, Mary Lou! I'm going for help."

And then, with the sound-track music pursuing him like the Furies, Steve hurries out of the house and down the front walk. In the next scene, we see him in the local police station, where the local police officer is sprawled complacently behind his desk, smiling with sceptical indulgence as Steve pours out his fervent tale.

"I swear to you, Joe," Steve is saying urgently, punching the officer's desk with his forefinger for emphasis, "It's *not Mary Lou!*"

The cop stretches and yawns pacifically. "Now there, Steve. Don't tell me you been riding your tractor in the noonday sun without a hat again?"

Steve rises to his full height, white-lipped, furious, dignified. "Listen to me. It looks like Mary Lou. It walks like Mary Lou. Shucks, it's even got her voice. But the things she's saying, Officer Dogma, I swear to you – " He looks around furtively, then lowers his voice to an ominous whisper. "They don't sound a bit like my girl."

"No?" The police officer smiles politely, but with a trace of mockery pulling at the corner of his mouth. "Who *does* she sound like, Steve?"

"Joe – Officer Dogma – I know this seems crazy, but . . . but she sounds like – like an airline stewardess!"

A close-up on Steve's face, terrified but convinced, followed by a close-up shot of Officer Dogma looking bemusedly stunned, as though someone had just struck him across the face with a frozen fillet of lemon sole. Another thrill of nervous music, as the scene fades out.

Cut to a night-time shot of the officer still looking bemused and meditative as he drives his car up the driveway of a darkened bungalow, turns off the ignition, then pulls the emergency brake noisily before killing the headlights.

We follow him out of the car, up the front walk, then wait with him as he rummages in the moonlight to find his keys in the pocket of his uniform slacks. At last, he inserts the key in the lock.

Next we follow the same Officer Dogma surreptitiously making his way through the interior of the darkened house, then into the bedroom, where a single bedside lamp is burning.

In the bed, her attractive nightgown-clad shoulders protruding above the snowy boundary of the bed sheet, lies a pretty thirtyish woman, reading a paperback. As Joe leans over the bed to kiss her cheek, she does not look up from her book, but flinches slightly and, almost imperceptibly, pulls away.

Joe notices, but pretends not to notice. He removes his uniform, hangs it up carefully on a coat hanger, then takes a crumpled pack of Lucky Strikes from the pocket of his shirt before hanging it up, and sets the cigarette pack down on his bedside table. Then, clad in his undershirt and shorts, he crawls into bed beside the woman, and regards her for a long moment before speaking.

JOE: Hey, Lizabeth, you sulking now? Put down that book, honey, and kill the light.

(*Before he can reach across her to extinguish the bedside lamp beside her, she strikes his arm away, still feigning absorption in her book.*)

ELIZABETH (*flatly*): I regret to inform you that, at this time, sexual overtures will not be encouraged.

JOE: Say what?

(*Startled, he pulls away, and looks at her from an alarmed distance.*)

"Currently in our marriage," recited Elizabeth, "we are experiencing some turbulence. For this reason, you are advised to remain on your side of the bed, with your undershorts securely fastened."

At this point, if I remember correctly, there was yet another chord of suspenseful music, as Joe regarded his wife with a replay of the same struck-by-a-lemon-sole expression he'd exhibited to Steve, back in the police station.

"Look," he said at last, cagily narrowing his eyes. "Let's *talk* about it, whatever it is." And he reached for the crumpled pack of Luckies on the end table beside him.

"At this time, you are requested to extinguish all smoking materials."

Quick as a shot, Joe's hand retracted, and he gave Elizabeth another look of horrified alarm as she continued her expressionless announcement.

"Once, however, your wife has switched off her bedside lamp and has achieved her sleeping state, cigarette smoking will be permitted. Except, of course, in those parts of the house specifically designated as no-smoking areas, including the furnace room and the children's sleeping quarters."

At this point, without warning, Elizabeth throws back the cover and gets out of the bed, padding purposefully across the room on bare feet to the clothes closet.

"Lizabeth," Joe whimpers, watching her, "once and for all, what's eating you?"

He watches and we watch as Elizabeth, in something like a mechanical trance, begins removing hangers of clothing from her side of the closet, flinging them emphatically but unhurriedly onto the bed.

"Elizabeth?"

At last she pauses and turns to him, a bouclé suit on a hanger in her hand. "In a very short time, I will be arriving at the end of my patience. On behalf of myself and the children, I would like to say it's been our pleasure to live with you until today."

Electrified with surprise and horror, Officer Dogma leaps out of the bed, and finds himself standing stupidly in the middle of the room, flat-footed and pleading.

"Elizabeth! Please, honey, don't go! I mean it. You can't leave me."

There was another pause at this point, longer and more dramatic, as Elizabeth regarded her husband with a cool and clear-eyed stare. Then, after an almost endless moment, she began picking her clothes off the bed, and returning them to the closet.

Sweating with relief, Joe bounded over to her and began, moistly, to kiss her hand.

"Thank you, Lizabeth! Honey, thank you!"

Coldly, however, she pulled her hand away from him, and in a white shaft of moonlight that flooded the room, she regarded him with a remote glacial stare.

ELIZABETH: Please make your exit this evening through the door provided at the front of the house.

JOE (*taken aback*): Exit? What exit? I thought you'd decided that –

ELIZABETH: And kindly check all drawers, closets, and underground storage areas for any and all personal belongings you may have brought with you into this marriage.

JOE (*shrieking*): Elizabeth! You mean now you're giving *me* the gate? Just like that? And you won't even tell me why?

Eerily caught by moonlight, Elizabeth turns to him with a seraphic smile, radiant yet oddly impersonal. "Thank you for choosing to marry Elizabeth Dogma. This is the termination of Joe and Elizabeth's marriage. Should you require any divorce information, kindly check with the lawyer's office, conveniently located in the – "

At this moment, I must have been groaning and twitching violently, for suddenly I felt the cool hand of a stewardess, shaking me gently awake.

"Thank God you woke me up," I said, my face bathed in a cold glistening sweat. "I was having the most horrifying dream. It was about women, you see, nice normal women whose bodies have been inexplicably invaded by the souls of automatons.

"Normal sunny personalities obliterated by a terrible impersonal civility. Individuated modes of speech wiped out in favor of a kind of Fortran language that reminded me of nothing so strongly as the sort of vocal pattern you find aboard commercial aircraft, broadcast over the inflight intercom by the voices of . . . "

As the stewardess stared back at me with a flinty little smile, her grip tightened convulsively on my arm, and I felt my words die in my throat.

The voices of airline stewardesses. That was what I'd started to say, and it was clear that she knew it. Knew it and resented it because, of course, these days they insist on being referred to as flight attendants.

The Invasion of the Airline Stewardesses. Just a crazy dream... or was it?

"For your continued travelling pleasure, a complimentary alcoholic beverage will be served to you at this time," said the flight attendant, still with the glint of her knowing smile. "Please remain seated for your own safety and comfort, with your seat belt securely fastened."

As she hurried away (too quickly?) to get me a sedative glass of wine (and perhaps to alert the rest of the crew that someone on board was on to their plan for world domination?), I reached casually into the pocket located directly in front of my seat for the safety-features card provided for my information while travelling and scanned it quickly to see what it might have to say about the possibility of the type of eerie inflight invasion I was beginning to hypothesize.

Just as I'd suspected, there wasn't a breath of a mention. Damned clever, these flight attendants.

A Licence to Print Slogans

We live, as I'm sure you're aware, in a world where every flat surface is an excuse for imparting information. A world in which no matchbook cover is complete without the vital statistics of the Lesser Prairie Ptarmigan, no sugar packet looks dressed without a readout on the forest productivity of the B.C. Interior, and no paper placemat is considered worth its ketchup stains if it doesn't tell you the names of at least thirteen cocktails that are made with a whiskey base.

Now, I'm willing to overlook all that. But what really *does* get me is one of the oldest offenders of them all: car licence plates, and the one-line slogans embossed thereon.

For one thing, does anybody know who comes up with the respective motto for each North American province and state? For instance, what savant decided B.C. was "Beautiful"? Who, exactly, says Pennsylvania is the "Keystone State"? And what do people who come from Missouri really expect to see when they demand "Show Me"?

Something else I'd like to know is how it ever got determined that licence-plate slogans were necessary to begin with. Europeans seem to get by without them. You don't see French cars proclaiming the "Cancan Country". Danes don't designate their nation as "Home of Hamlet". Nor do the Irish insist on calling themselves the "Snake-Free State".

No, it's just North Americans who seem compelled to turn each and every auto into a gas-powered booster for its particular region of origin.

And another thing...for whom are these self-congratulatory sayings intended? Native British Columbians must *know* the place is "Beautiful". And surely out-of-province motorists wouldn't decide to make the long drive to the coast on the insubstantial information they get from a passing licence plate. It's just another case of preaching to the already converted while failing to convince anyone else.

But the absolutely *worst* aspect of the whole licence-plate embarrassment (which I refer to, quite unhyperbolically, as our National Disgrace) is the terrible things licence-plate slogans reveal about us as a people.

In Canada, licence-plate mottoes come in two categories. The first is the blatantly touristic. Which is why we are confronted on the highways by Nova Scotians – a classy people with a proud history – driving around advertising "Canada's Atlantic Playground". How tacky. While at the other end of the country, Albertans – not so classy or historical perhaps, but still better than this – are calling themselves "Wildrose Country".

Oh, come now. When you think of Alberta, is it ever wild roses that come to mind? What about "Creationism Country", or "Land of Blue-Eyed Sheiks"?

The second and even more pernicious class of licence-plate slogan is the hortatory. Licence plates that cry out: Prevent Forest Fires, Buckle Up, Don't Just Sit There, Do Something!

Not surprisingly, Calvinistic Ontario leads the pack in this category. For years Ontario plates have ordered us to "Keep It Beautiful". They don't specify what, nor do they explain how it got to be beautiful in the first place without our help. "Keep It Beautiful". That's all.

More recently, a revamped Ontario plate has come on the scenario, but it's still demanding action. "Yours To Discover" is the new watchword. Not, If You Feel Like Discovering, or If You Happen To Find Yourself Discovering By Accident Some Day. Uh-uh. Yours to discover. Pronto. That's an order, soldier.

Then there are the anomalous – and slightly ominous – licence-plate slogans that defy classification. Quebec, for instance, which declares darkly, "Je me souviens." I remember *what*, precisely? Nothing nice; you can be sure of that.

But my own personal favorite has got to be the plate of the

Great State of New Hampshire, which prescribes "Live Free or Die". Gulp. Let me tell you, when I find myself driving behind one of *those* guys, or in the next lane, I get myself out of there but quick. I mean, suppose this person decides he isn't living free enough? Does he plan to take me with him when he goes?

Besides, if this crazed New Hampshirite and I *did* crash through the Guardrail of Life, and wound up in that Great Collector Lane in the Sky, what do you suppose we'd find up there? You got it. The Pearly Gates, proudly emblazoned with the motto: "God's Country".

A Lesson in Horticulture

The world, I realize more and more as I grow older, is full of baffling and inexplicable occurrences. And the more baffling and inexplicable the occurrence is, the more men and women will attempt to make sense of it, to explain the mystery away, or – at the very least – to adduce a moral from what may have been, in actuality, merely a totally freakish and random happening.

Never has this human tendency to generalize and to moralize presented itself more vividly to me than on an autumn night, some time ago, in the Year of Our Lord 19—, in the city of T——.

A group of us had dropped in on a friend who'd just moved into new quarters, and we'd brought with us various gifts appropriate to a housewarming: several ashtrays (although all of us expected to give up smoking momentarily, and had indeed already taken the important preliminary step of giving up buying); an engagingly kitsch crocheted poodle to cover the telephone; and a lachrymose-looking house plant of indeterminate breed.

"Oh my God," exclaimed our friend as he unwrapped the florist paper from the plant. "Take it out of here. I'm death to these things, I really am."

"Come, come," the donor of the plant scolded. "A little water twice a week and a sunny window. That's all a plant asks."

But our friend shook his head with dogged insistence. "I'm telling you, it won't survive a week with me. Take a look at this thumb. Not only isn't it green, but can you see there's the faint outline of a skull and crossbones on it? This is the thumb of a planticide."

Several of the rest of us laughed the high-pitched laugh of recognition. There were those among us who felt exactly the same way about his or her blighted record as a horticulturalist. I myself still firmly believed that what my begonia had succumbed to was a yeast infection. Another friend told an hilariously funny story about realizing that her prayer-plant was in trouble when, in addition to praying, it began to light candles.

But the friend who'd brought the plant as a gift still failed to join in the general hilarity. "A plant is easy to keep happy," he declared. "Especially if you talk to it."

A chorus of jeers greeted that remark.

"Oh, yes," someone hooted. "Talk to your plant. Tell it to drink all its water, because there are starving violets in Africa who'd be grateful for it."

"Or read to it," someone else suggested. "How about *Princess Daisy*? Or *Leaves of Grass*?"

Everyone was laughing uproariously by now, with the exception of the plant-lover, and another friend, Cutler, who stood lounging by the mantelpiece and who had, thus far, contributed absolutely nothing to the conversation.

"Cutler," I said, giving him a nudge, "you're being uncharacteristically silent. What do you think? Does it help plants to talk to them?"

Dusk was falling rapidly, and the only illumination in the room came from the blaze in the hearth, which cast eerie patterns of light and shadow on our faces as we sat before it. Something about the way that Cutler stared long and hard into the fire before answering made me shiver with apprehension.

"Perhaps so," Cutler said at length. "The question is, does talking to plants help *you*?"

The rest of us exchanged glances. Typical Cutler, these cryptic utterances. The week before, apparently, he'd caused a stir over lunch some place by hinting that a rising vogue in pasta might possibly be connected to the increased incidence of incest.

"Great Scot, Cutler." Our host prodded new life into the fire with a poker. "Don't tell me you're an expert on plant communication, in addition to all your other areas of knowledge."

"I know something about the subject," replied the other tersely. "Enough, anyway, to be wary."

Again I shivered, as if with a chill, although the room was warm enough. To me, Cutler's tone suggested dark mysteries, better left undisclosed.

"I knew a man once," Cutler went on, "called Joe. And if anyone could attest to the dangerous consequences of learning to talk to house plants, that man is Joe. *Was*, Joe, I should perhaps say. For his experiences have changed him, almost into another man."

"Oh, come now," protested our plant-loving friend, somewhat nervously. "It can't have been as dire as all that."

"Wait," said Cutler simply, "and judge for yourself."

There was, we all sensed, an air of absolute conviction about him with respect to the matter. Cutler may have been bluffing the other day about the pasta, but tonight he was in deadly earnest about plants.

"Joe," he began his story, "was a typical apartment-dwelling bachelor. Much like our friend here" – and Cutler indicated the companion whose apartment we were in – "until one day, when a neighbor brought over a house plant. Just as a friendly gesture, you understand.

"Like our host, Joe was reluctant to assume responsibility for one of our rooted friends, and told his well-meaning benefactress so. But the neighbor insisted that Joe give plant-owning a try, and by way of parting advice suggested to him that he would do well to talk to his new acquisition.

"Talk to a plant? What in heaven's name about? Joe hadn't the faintest idea. His first attempts at persiflage were awkward, fumbling. . . . 'Hi there,' he'd say. 'Wet enough for you? What's the latest dirt?'

"Gradually, however, he began to relax, to open up to the plant. And to talk about his own problems, which, not surprisingly for a young man in his situation, centred around women.

"Joe had never had very much confidence with respect to the fairer sex, had never really known how to get on with women. And in some curious way – perhaps because learning to talk to the plant had come with such difficulty – he found it possible to expound upon the subject to his little potted friend.

" 'I don't know,' Joe would explain earnestly, 'I just never seemed to hit it off with girls. Back in high school, it was my buddies who dated the really great chicks. . . .' Eventually, Joe would glance at his watch, startled to see how the time had flown.

" 'Hey, look,' he'd apologize to the plant, 'I didn't mean to keep you up so late.'

"But the plant never looked as though it minded Joe's late-night confidences. Nor did it ever appear bored by anything he had to say.

"In fact, in some strange way, Joe began to realize that the plant was providing him with a species of sympathy – yes, even intimacy – without precedent or parallel in his experience of the two-legged world. In this humble house plant, in other words, Joe came to feel he'd located his one true friend."

As Cutler paused to wet his lips on a tumbler of Perrier-with-a-twist that our host had handed him in the course of his narrative, the rest of us shifted in our seats, less with physical discomfort than with a hint of incipient disaster, as we began to sense, to a man and a woman, that more lay ahead in the story of Joe – much, much more. And some of it of a decidedly sobering nature.

"But peculiar as that bond between man and plant might seem," Cutler continued, once his thirst had been slaked, "far more peculiar still was the bond beginning to form between plant and man.

"It all came rushing to the fore one fateful evening, after Joe had brought a young lady back to his apartment for a nightcap – and whatever else he thought he might get."

At this, the men in the room all averted their eyes with guilty embarrassment. Each one of them had, at one time or another, been in Joe's situation – lonely, lecherous, opportunistic. And to each one of them, therefore, there was a quality of *déjà entendu* embodied in the series of events Cutler next detailed.

"Once Joe had the girl – Patty was her name – seated on the couch, with a good stiff drink in her hand, he tried to make what he termed 'a suave move', intending to switch out the lamp behind her and to get his arm around her shoulder, all in one fluid gesture.

"But Patty was having none of that. In a gesture far more fluid than anything Joe could ever hope to aspire to, she leapt off the couch, grabbed up her coat, and dashed what remained of her drink into her suitor's face, all before slamming the apartment door on him and running off into the night."

Now it was the women's turn to shift their feet with embarrassment, as each one silently recollected an instance when she had
behaved as impulsively – and perhaps even as athletically – as
Patty, bolting away at the first manifestation of interest from the
male whose attention she had spent all evening trying to arouse.

No wonder, I reflected to myself, that men and women were
getting nowhere on the road to mutual understanding. On the
other hand, if Joe was really half as unlikely as Cutler had
described him, perhaps Patty should not be blamed for the
vehemence of her rejection.

"Joe was devastated," Cutler declared, drawing me back firmly
into the web of his narrative. "How many times had an evening
ended in exactly that same depressing sequence? The sprint from
the sofa, the drink in his face, the sound of high heels clattering
away in the dark?

"As he wiped Scotch-and-soda from his cheek with his handkerchief, he could not help giving vent to a heartfelt expletive. 'Nuts!'
said Joe bitterly.

" 'Nuts is right,' came the prompt replay. 'Sheesh, but did you
blow it, buddy-boy.'

"Startled, Joe dropped his handkerchief and whirled to face the
direction from which the voice had come. There was nothing
there. Nothing but the living-room window sill, and upon that
window sill, his solitary plant.

" 'I mean, you drop fifty bucks on dinner, not to mention gas
and parking . . . ' The voice – breezy, nasal, and streetwise – was
unfamiliar to Joe, although not entirely. As he continued to hunt
frantically for the source, it occurred to him that the voice he was
hearing sounded more than a little like Bugs Bunny.

" 'And *still* you come up empty,' the mocking buzz-saw tones
continued. 'What a maroon.'

" 'Who are you?' Joe demanded, almost beside himself. 'Where
are you?'

" 'Sheesh, buddy-boy, what are you, blind as well as dumb?
You're looking right at me.'

" 'It – it can't be!' Joe gasped. 'My plant? Talking to me?'

" 'Why not?' the plant wanted to know. 'You talk to me, I talk to
you. Fair is fair, right?'

' "But . . . how did you learn?'

" 'Where do you think, pal? From you.'

" 'You couldn't have. We don't sound a bit alike.'

" 'Thanks. Actually, I picked up a little extra vocabulary from the TV – you know, the Saturday morning cartoons? Plus a lot of insight that went right by *you*, evidently.'

" 'What are you talking about?'

" 'He wants to know what I'm talking about,' observed the plant despairingly, to no one in particular. 'This is the third chick you've brought back here in a week. And the third time you've fanned right out.'

" 'Can I help it if Patty's a prude?' demanded Joe, stung.

" 'Prude nothing. She's dying for it. Just like the rest of them. Problem is, your technique's all wrong.'

" 'Oh sure,' said Joe. 'You're in a great spot to hand out romantic advice. Someone who leaves the whole thing to bees.'

" 'Are you going to listen to me?' the plant demanded. 'Or do you want to shell out for free dinners forever?'

" 'Look, I know about women,' said Joe.

" 'Oh sure you do,' said the plant. 'All the way back since high school, right?'

"Well, that got to Joe. Wounded by the plant's betrayal of his late-night confidences, he nevertheless let it have its say, and while it hurt to hear a catalogue of his amatory deficiencies, he had to admit, in the end, that the plant had a few points.

" 'All right,' he muttered sullenly. 'What should I do differently?'

"The plant cleared its throat in a businesslike way and then, for the better part of an hour, it held forth on the art of seduction, with an air of crisp detachment that kept Joe alternately entranced and unnerved.

"Where had the plant picked up all this lore? More important, whence had come the quality of sangfroid that went with the stunning information? Joe could only conclude that the theoretical nature of the subject, from a plant's point of view, resulted inevitably in a certain distancing from the emotional heart of the matter. But one fact was undeniable – the plant definitely knew its stuff.

"After a few more heart-to-heart sessions of a similar nature, the plant deemed Joe ready to put his new techniques into practice. Accordingly, he made another date with Patty, overcoming her initial reluctance for a rematch with promises of dinner at one of that city's most exclusive eating establishments.

"After dinner – a mellow affair made mellower by two bottles of very good Cabernet – Joe succeeded in inveigling Patty back to his apartment once more."

Cutler paused, purely for effect this time, as the Perrier-with-a-twist had all long since been consumed. The rest of us were, by now, malleable clay in his hands. As rapt and open-mouthed as Joe imbibing wisdom from the plant, we were mutely absorbing Cutler's words with absolute fascination. Having satisfied himself that this was indeed the case, Cutler once more resumed his narrative.

"This evening was a completely different experience for Joe – and for Patty, too, as a matter of fact. As he moulded the attractive young woman rapidly and deftly to his desires, Joe couldn't but marvel at just how thoroughly the plant knew its romantic business, and how effectively it had coached him to put into practice the theoretical abstractions it had presented.

"In short, Joe had an absolutely marvellous time with Patty that night, and would have been perfectly content to go on having marvellous times with her for many months to come. However, the plant's wisdom decreed otherwise.

" 'Do yourself a personal favor, buddy-boy,' the plant advised, after Joe had dated Patty on three consecutive weekends. 'Play the field a little. A guy who's been on the chewed end of the pencil for as long as *you* have where dames are concerned oughta make up for some lost time.'

"And so, Joe played the field. He played at least half a dozen fields, to be exact, among them fields named Alice, Myra, Lee, Lyn, and Sheila. Under the plant's tutelage, with each one of these women he came close to an abundance of joy heretofore unknown to him, and with each he was more than ready to call a halt to philandering and linger awhile, as each woman successively hoped he might.

"But the plant was having none of that, and went on insisting that Joe play the field. Until, at last, Joe played all the way into the life of a married woman named Cynthia.

"Around about the third week that they'd been dating intensively – the maximum period that the plant would allow Joe to confine himself to one woman before exhorting him to move on – Cynthia made an ominous announcement to Joe over lunch.

" 'Since I met you, Joe,' she said, 'I realize how hopelessly empty my marriage is. What would you say if I decided to leave him?'

" 'Leave him?' Joe echoed, beginning to sweat a little. 'Cynthia, don't you think we better slow down a bit?'

" 'Why? When it's you I want? Day after day, week after week, year after year together – '

" 'Did you say year after year?'

" 'Of course. Joe, isn't that what you want, too?'

"What Joe might have wanted wasn't, of course, the point. What really mattered was what the plant wanted for him. Nervous and profusely apologetic, he bolted from the restaurant, then rushed home to consult the plant as to what should be done.

" 'So?' shrugged the plant nonchalantly. 'If she dumps the old man, great. It'll make it more convenient for you to see her when you want.'

" 'But I thought I was supposed to be playing the field.'

" 'You are. First you sneak off on her to see other chicks; then, when her time is up, you dump her. See? No problem.'

" 'No problem!' Joe was aghast. 'Cynthia's in love with me and ready to ruin her life.'

"The plant stared at him without comprehension. 'Yeah, so? As long as you have your fun, where does the problem come in?'

"Joe gasped. 'What are you – inhuman?'

"As soon as the words were out of his mouth, he realized that of course it was so. The plant was, when all was said and done, merely an invertebrate. And, for all its worldliness and predatory know-how, it had neither a conscience nor a soul to raise it to the realms of the higher beings. Why, all this time he, Joe, had been carrying out the orders of an unfeeling vegetable. Just exactly what did that make *him*?

"None of these fine ethical points did Joe bother to argue out with the plant. Instead, he merely voiced his agreement that Cynthia would have to be gotten rid of in due course, all the while silently resolving that it would, in due course, be the plant who would have to go.

"The very next night, Joe made good his resolve. Pretending to be removing the plant from its accustomed sill only for a little light dusting, he managed to whisk it speedily into a garbage bag, and hurry it down the back stairs, to the place where a trash can stood behind the apartment building.

"From inside the bag came the plant's cries, muffled yet decidedly apprehensive. 'Hey, what's going on here? Buddy-boy? Hey, cut the kidding, and tell me what goes.'

"Joe raised the lid of the trash can. 'Sorry,' he said tersely. 'It's the only way.' And he hurled the plant into the can, clamped down the lid, then turned on his heel to rush back up the stairs.

"The plant's angry imprecations echoing from the depths of the garbage can followed him all the way into his apartment.

" 'I'll get you for this!' came the hysterical threats. 'I made you, buddy-boy, and I can unmake you, too. You hear me, buddy-boy? You'll pay!'"

There was a collective sigh of relief as Cutler reached this point in his tale. No one in the room had any sympathy for the plant any more, and we were delighted to hear that Joe was rid of its evil influence forever.

"In the weeks that followed," Cutler resumed, "Joe worked at getting his personal life back on the tracks and retrieving his banished self-respect. First, he suspended his relationship with Cynthia, whom he did not love, reassuring her – over her copious tears – that she was far better off to stay with her husband, or leave him to pursue an independent life. Then Joe abandoned his casual entanglements with numerous other women, and made a vow to himself that he would engage in further romantic dalliance only after a period of abstinence and self-purification.

"The new Spartan rigor of his private life seemed to redound beneficially upon his career, which he'd been sorely neglecting. Several weeks after disposing of the malevolent plant, he found himself promoted to a new and more prestigious position in the company where he worked, as a direct result of the extra time his emptied social calendar had given him to work late and on the weekends. With the promotion came a commensurately new and more prestigious office.

"This development, Joe reflected as he hurried down the office corridor to inspect his new quarters, could hardly have come at a more opportune time. Following months of overindulgence –

under the plant's orchestration – the weeks of abstinence were proving onerous, and libidinous fantasies (again, he blamed the plant for such a tawdry legacy) had begun to take their toll upon his recently cultivated moral fibre. A change in duties, he therefore hoped, might serve to keep him on the straight and narrow until he had fully re-acclimatized himself to the wintery conditions of his new celibate life, which was exactly like the old celibate life he'd led before the plant's arrival – with the exception that now he had some lascivious memories to torment him.

"But his hopes of moral triumph were short-lived. When he reached the doorway of his new office, he was met by the sight of Louise, his shapely new secretary, bent prettily over a carton of stationery supplies, as she selected materials with which to outfit the drawers of his new and more prestigious desk.

" 'It looks great, Louise, just great,' said Joe enthusiastically and ambiguously, trying to keep an audible leer out of his voice.

"Louise straightened up. 'I'm so glad you like it. I've pretty well got everything set up...carpets, lamps, some plants...' She gestured in a general way around the room. 'But if you see anything missing, just buzz me in the outer office and let me know.'

"He couldn't help devouring her exquisite legs with his eyes as she left the room. Nor could he resist the occasional lip-licking thought as he arranged the few desk ornaments he'd brought with him from his old and less prestigious office.

" 'Imagine rubbing suntan oil on those long, smooth legs,' he mused, temporarily forgetting his vow as he set out his blotter and desk calendar. 'Great, just great...'

" 'I'll say it's great, buddy-boy.'

"At the echoing of his thoughts, Joe started as violently as an ambushed deer. 'Wh-what? Who said that?'

"Surely, he reasoned desperately, his eyes darting around the room in frantic quest of the source of the voice, he was imagining things. Surely he hadn't heard what he thought he'd heard, at least not from any corporeal quarter. Instead, in all probability, it had been the voice of his own guilty conscience, punishing him with aural phantoms for the crime of permitting himself lewd imaginings about the lovely Louise. Hadn't that been it?

" 'All kidding aside, buddy-boy. You've got it made in the shade with that Louise babe if you want.'

"This time, there was no mistaking the particularly brassy timbre of that voice, or the locality from which it came. Perched on the window sill of his new and more prestigious office, exactly where Louise had placed it, was his nemesis of old, the lechery-minded plant, hardly the worse for its sojourn in the trash – give or take a few crumpled leaves – and so ineluctably *there* that there was no point in the world in Joe's pretending that he'd been hearing things.

" 'You!' Joe bellowed horribly. 'How on earth did you get in here?'

" 'I mean, that's the beauty of getting it on with the secretary, right?' the plant went on, oblivious to Joe's distress. 'She starts making demands, you just give her the gate.'

" 'How did you find me?' Joe demanded, on the brink of tears.

" 'Come on, buddy-boy. Did you really think it would be that easy? Into the garbage, over and out?'

"Terrified, Joe raced to the intercom on his desk and sounded the buzzer repeatedly. 'Louise!' he cried. 'Get in here!'

" 'That's the old spirit, buddy-boy!' the plant applauded. 'Make your move on her right away.'

"Louise appeared at the door, anxious and inquiring, then stopped short at the sight of Joe's horrified face.

" 'Anything the matter?'

" 'This plant!' Joe gesticulated wildly toward the window sill. 'How did it get here?'

" 'I . . . beg your pardon?' said Louise.

" 'Get it out of here!' Joe was aware that his voice was high-pitched, even shrill. 'Kill it!'

" 'Now, just a second here,' the plant protested.

"Joe wheeled on it, shouting angrily, 'Shut up, just shut up!'

" 'Why, you're hysterical!' cried Louise.

" 'No!' Joe declared. As he advanced on her, his eyes bugging, his face blotched with emotion, Louise shrank from him. 'It's not me, it's that plant. Don't listen to anything it has to say, Louise.'

"With a sob of terror, Louise sprang from the room in search of the company medical team.

"In the end, the decision was taken to send Joe away for a nice long rest. In fact, as far as I know, he's still resting. Free of the burdens of executive life, and the demands of a hectic social calendar.

"Word has it that Joe has managed to make a new life for himself at the rest home, sharing gladly in the chores patients are given to do around the place – in the laundry room, the kitchen, even the lavatories. But, curiously, there's one aspect of this volunteer labor that totally repulses him: under no circumstance will Joe bring himself to work in the asylum gardens. The very suggestion is enough to send him into a terrified frenzy, quite heart-rending to behold."

With that, Cutler spread his hands to indicate that his tale had ended and gazed at each member of the assembly with a world-weary little smile.

"Well?" he demanded. "What did I tell you? Isn't Joe's grisly fate a lesson to us all?"

By this time, evening had succeeded twilight and the fire had shrunk down to a few faint embers, which cast ever-lengthening and even more sinister shadows on the gloomy walls.

I stole a furtive glance at my companions, whose ashen faces all gave assurance that each one of them was as sobered as I.

"Yes," answered our host at length, with a jaunty bravado he clearly did not feel. "A lesson, all right. But a lesson in *what*?"

"Why, in the laws of nature, of course," someone else replied. "Haven't you been listening? Plainly, in talking to his plant, Joe encouraged it to give advice above its station, advice that brought Joe to ruin."

"No, that's not it at all!" spoke up the friend whose gift of a plant in the first place had occasioned Cutler's story. "There's nothing wrong with talking to plants. Joe's problems were purely internal, wholly connected to his psychology. After banishing the plant, he leapt too frantically at corporate success. In the end, he cracked under the pressure of his rapid promotion."

The women in the group, as one, shouted that suggestion down. "It has nothing to do with nature, or career," they chorused. "How typical of men, that they can't see the real fault. Joe's value system was corrupt, that's all. Live by the little black book, die by the little black book. The plant is only the symbol of Joe's lecherous inner self."

"What do you say, Cutler?" our host inquired, turning back to Cutler, who continued to meet all our speculations with the same world-weary little smile with which he had concluded his yarn.

"Which of us has rightly guessed the lesson your story illustrates?"

But Cutler only went on smiling in his silent, maddening way, and would enlighten us no further.

Gradually, we all began to shake off the sense of foreboding that his story had inspired, and by the end of the evening we were a light-hearted and voluble group of friends once more, able to enter into a lively game of Space Invaders with cries of eager enthusiasm.

Which is not to say, however, that Cutler's cautionary tale failed to leave its indelible mark upon at least one of us.

The next day, my travels happened to take me back past the same apartment building in which we'd heard the chilling story of the night before.

Outside our host's apartment, on the balcony, which fronted on the street, was a garbage can, full to the brim with the detritus of moving in. On top of the pile of refuse stood the plant our friend had given him the previous evening. Beside the plant, a well-thumbed black notebook marked "Phone Numbers". And beside that, a rejected paperback book entitled *How To Rise Up the Career Ladder Once You've Given Up Chasing Girls*.

Someone, clearly, was covering all of his bets.

CELLULITE

Speaking of computers (and I could swear you were just about to), I can't help being amused to hear that this relatively trivial development is now touted as the most significant technological advance since the printing press. People who are truly in the know know different. The real revolution in science has come about as a result of the invention of cellulite.

For those who have spent the last few years in a solipsistic haze (the only possible explanation for ignorance in this area), let me hasten to explain that cellulite – a growth industry in every sense of that phrase – is the collective term for those bumps and wiggly rivulets of fat found principally on the thighs and buttocks. Of women. Only women. (Got that? There'll be an exam later in the term.)

If you are one of the afflicted who gaze bleakly down at your once-lithe nether limbs that now look as though they have been recently re-upholstered in golfball-cover material, no doubt the first (printable) comment that will rise to your lips is: "But where did this *come* from? I exercise; I subsist entirely on a diet of defatted celery hearts and Diet Ramlösa; I take steam so often that I need malaria shots. And still I've got cellulite. Where does it come from?"

Where does it come from, you ask. It comes from France.

Like everything else that's bad for you, including *crème fraîche* and Françoise Sagan novels. Cellulite was invented by the French, perfected there, and then exported – although, of course, you know that the French keep the best for themselves and send us only the dregs.

But considering that cellulite is a recently acquired taste in North America, and indeed was not even commonly found in most homes before 1979, its current ubiquitousness is all the more astonishing. What accounts for this sudden and overwhelming demand?

One clue, perhaps, lies in the name itself. *"Cell*ulite." As in "sell". (You savvy? That could show up on the exam too.) An entire ancillary industry has sprung up around cellulite, a bewildering array of books, exercises, and stringent diets all promising (but not exactly in so many legally binding words) to deal with the problem.

My own favorite in this canon of cellulite combatants is an absolutely super jim-dandy cellucidal massage mitt that I bought, which fits over your hand like a set of vinyl knuckles, and comes with a bar of absolutely super jim-dandy cellucidal soap with which you curry your flanks like a racehorse for five minutes a day in the shower, since, as the accompanying literature states, a mere five is enough to ensure a return to smooth and beautiful skin.

Well, they're right about one thing. Five minutes is enough. More than enough. Otherwise, there is no discernible outcome. This massage mitt and soap cost in excess of twenty dollars and, it goes without saying, also come from France.

However, I wouldn't like to leave you with the impression that the entire motivation behind the invention of cellulite and its antidotes was crass commercialism. *Pas du tout*, as Françoise Sagan might say. There are, in fact, some very socially responsible reasons behind the development of this dermatological phenomenon. These I like to refer to as The Peacetime Uses of Cellulite.

Foremost among them is the very necessary perpetuation of differences between the sexes. The threat (not yet realized, thank God) of equal pay for women in the work force, as well as the expanding role of men in child-rearing and domestic labor, and the increasing presence of females in top-echelon corporate positions (although, again, not too many, thank God), have all served to blur the God-ordained lines of division between the two genders, and have generally created the very misleading impression that the lot of womankind is improving. The existence of cellulite, a female-only affliction (remember I told you that could show up on the exam) helps to reassure us that progress has demonstrably not occurred.

Secondly, women have, throughout history, enjoyed some pretty cheap laughs over the fact that men are the ones who tend to go bald. The newly recognized existence of cellulite helps men to even up an old score.

From a purely practical point of view as well, cellulite has arrived at a timely moment for the health-craze industry, recently thrown into a bit of a tizzy over the bad name that has accrued to slenderizing, thanks to the epidemic rise of *anorexia nervosa*. Once skinniness begins to look psychotic, where can the exercise empire turn for inspiration? Why, to cellulite, of course – to the emphasis on the quality, rather than the quantity, of flesh.

Conveniently, insurance companies are currently discussing adjusting their weight-for-height tables upward by about five pounds in each category, possibly as an acknowledgement that the idea of female muscularity, with its connotations of firmed and toned flesh, has gained respectability. Could the signs be any clearer than that? If the twentieth century belongs to Canada (notice I said *if*), then surely the twenty-first will belong to cellulite.

So. If that's going to be the wobbly, jiggly, tapioca-like shape of things to come, I say let's learn to make the best of it. For one thing, statistics are running in our favor, if nothing else is. The group which cellulite strikes with vengeance – women in their mid-thirties – happens, at the moment, to be the largest demographic constituency in Canada.

If we play our cards right, we might even manage to turn cellulite into a rage, so that it may soon become *de rigueur* (as Françoise Sagan might also say) to look as though your entire lower body has been sculpted out of cottage cheese.

And even if we muff that hand, there is yet no need to despair. Think what cellulite, even in its present maligned form, has done for Canadian women. It's given us something we can all discuss with each other, now that Maggie Trudeau has dropped out of sight, and the pornography controversy is becoming old hat.

In addition, cellulite has helped discourage those superficial involvements with muscular young men, who would otherwise try to pick us up at the beach, had we not our protective covering of lumpy flesh to warn them away. Thus are we spared sensual, ego-building, titillating, and heartwarming encounters that would, in the end, only make us feel cheap and demeaned, as well as ruining us for the more mundane rigors of marriage.

And as if all those benefits were not enough, cellulite has served to unite all women as never before – the fat and the thin, the athletic and the sedentary, rich and poor, Leo and Taurus – in a bond of real sisterly self-loathing, as we all take a collective look at ourselves in the mirror in our shorts.

And you wanted to talk computers. I can't believe it. (Oh, by the way – good luck on the exam, eh?)

TALKING TO STRANGERS

In spite of the stern injunctions handed to us as children on our way to the playground or heading out alone to the movies for the first time, most of us have to spend a great deal of our life talking to strangers. And watching a group of people struggle against the silence in an elevator as they stare with feigned fascination at the floor numbers flashing by, or gaze down at their shoes as if counting the toe perforations were something they'd been meaning to get around to for some time, suggests compellingly that the long-ago parental dictum holds sway even into adulthood, and that we are, at some level, still nervous about talking to people we don't know.

One-Way Communication: A First Small Step for Man

Luckily, however, there are shrewd merchandisers out there, who – once they've perceived a gaping public need – are quickly able to fill it with a product designed to redress the problem.

In the case of talking to strangers, lasting relief has been provided in the form of the automobile bumper sticker, twentieth-century capitalism's ringing endorsement of John Donne's contention that no man is an island – not, at least, as long as he is travelling one of the nation's major highways.

The succinct instantaneousness of the bumper sticker is, of course, its major selling point. After all, if Andy Warhol is right and each of us has only fifteen minutes in which to be famous, it follows that we can't afford to waste very much of the precious allotment on merely introducing ourselves. A good bumper sticker can get the job done in a maximum of five seconds.

If you feel entitled to definitive proof of just how thorough and effective a bumper sticker can be in providing a quick comprehensive profile of the owner of the car to which it is affixed, try this simple experiment.

Purchase three bumper stickers at random from any five-and-dime store, lay them out on your living-room floor, then invite some friends over to see how quickly they can guess the sort of motorist who would choose each one, and the type of vehicle to which he or she would affix it.

This fun-filled game (not as time-consuming as bridge, less contentious than Trivial Pursuit) can form the basis of an impromptu party, with the addition of some light snacks and the beverage of your guests' choice. However you organize it, the evening will fly by, I assure you, on wings of good-natured hilarity, as you and your companions vie with each other to see who can make the most ingenious guesses.

Just to start you off on this entertaining pastime, let me suggest a few sample bumper stickers guaranteed to break the ice, and get the game rolling with the inexorable momentum of an eighteen-wheeler in high gear pelting down a six per cent grade.

1) "ONE NUCLEAR BOMB CAN RUIN YOUR WHOLE DAY"

Not difficult to divine the identity of the person who sports that mild-manneredly reproachful slogan on his back end, is it?

You're right if you guessed a Volvo owner, between the ages of thirty-five and forty-one, college-educated, married, with three children named Zack, Miranda, and Josiah (age two, a happy accident), none of whom took readily to toilet-training, and all of whom are encouraged to interrupt the grown-ups' conversation whenever they please.

Our Volvo owner is an urbanite (we'll call him Robert – never Bob), who has a wife, Lisa, who still wears her hair in a half-mast ponytail, and works part-time in a downtown settlement house, as well as being in charge of the parent duty-roster for Josiah's co-operative day-care centre.

Their dog, Eldridge, is a large setter-collie mix given to vomiting up large indeterminate messes on the next-door neighbors' front lawn, and the family has also had a succession of cats that continually run away.

In addition to nuclear disarmament, Robert believes in the vitality of the downtown core, summer sandlot baseball, and the enduring value of *GEO* magazine, a subscription to which he can be counted on to give every Christmas to someone. Robert also knows which bakery has the freshest bagels, who in the neigborhood has a manure-spreader he's willing to lend, and how to mend his own Birkenstocks.

For her part, Lisa can serve up tofu in a way that even the finickiest kids like, spots interesting-looking stones every time they go to the beach, gets car-sick unless one of the windows is left slightly open, and can never remember the lyrics to "Big Yellow Taxi".

It goes without saying that Robert and Lisa are Block Parents, that they buy *The New York Times* on Sunday, but seldom get around to reading it, that they plan to take a French course at the Community Centre in the fall, and that they only hope they can get it together to take the kids backpacking in Europe one summer, before it's – "you know, too late?"

2) "FEED JANE FONDA TO THE WHALES"

Whew. Of course, you realize immediately that what you're dealing with here is a Sonny Barger look-alike named Max, who likes to be referred to as "Mad Max", is usually seen in a too-tight black tee-shirt with "Born to Raise Hell" inscribed across the front in day-glo letters edged with flames, and has a deck of Export Plains wedged up one of the sleeves, next to his smallpox vaccination scar.

Max's vehicle of choice is a high-riding pickup by International Harvester painted to match his tee-shirt, with chrome-plated dual carbs, a plastic skull bobbling from the rearview mirror, and a sign on the door reading "Pussymobile".

Max is one of the few men living in Canada or anywhere else who uses the expression "poon-tang" with a straight face, and every time he goes out for a case of beer (which he inevitably refers to as a "two-four") he also comes home with yet another throwing knife.

He regards the game Space Invaders as a documentary of his

own life, believes the highest tribute that can be paid to any man is to say he has *cojones* (*cojones*-owners include George Wallace, Marvin Hagler, the late General Patton, and a guy Max knew one time in Deep River named "Crazy Lyle"), prides himself on the number of times he can make himself burp on a single beer, and believes that the best movie of all time is the *The Wild Bunch*.

Max has never met a woman he liked who wasn't tattooed, can't pass a dog on the street without kicking at it, regards black leather as formal wear, wishes he knew more people who were serious bikers, and believes that anything worth buying is available at Canadian Tire.

Max's formal education ended in grade nine when, already a strapping sixteen, he changed the second-term novel's title page to read *A Sale of Two Titties*, for which offence he was sent to the principal's office, where, he says, he flattened the principal with a left hook and never went back. He insists that the principal's version of the story, in which he was asked to clean out his desk and not return, is totally apocryphal.

Max still keeps in touch with his mother by phone every six months or so, although more and more in recent years he finds he has to repeat his name to her several times before she recognizes it. He also has a kid sister on the West Coast who considers morphine a recreational drug, and an uncle in Northern Manitoba who unscrewed his wooden leg one time and used it to knock his wife out cold. Otherwise, Max has no family he knows of.

Among Max's favorite pithy observations are: Hitler was very misunderstood; the only good thing that ever came from the West Indies was an empty boat; drinking rye all night with beer chasers makes him more alert; and the Unemployment Insurance expects you to cheat, otherwise their computers screw up.

Although he calls everybody "buddy", Max has very few people in his life he can actually count as friends, and occasionally he catches himself wondering why this is.

3) "HONK IF YOU LIKE INORGANIC CHEMISTRY"

Well, of course, who but a college student behind the wheel of what else except an antiquated Volkswagen beetle?

In point of fact, Meredith is in second-year arts. The reason the bumper sticker refers to chemistry is because she bought the car from her older brother Ian, who has always been a science nut. Actually, Meredith doesn't mind a bit if inorganic chemists honk at her from time to time – or organic ones, for that matter – since she's a very friendly girl who loves to wave back. Meredith stayed in her room all afternoon with the door closed the day she heard Karen Carpenter had died. Other than that, she can't recall ever having felt really depressed. Although, occasionally her sinuses hurt something awful, and she doesn't like the marks the braces left on her teeth, and at least once a day she catches herself wishing her eyelashes weren't so pale.

But these are minor downers in a world that abounds with so many desirable things, like for instance Professor Donegan, who teaches her twentieth-century American Lit class and is the most gorgeous man on earth, even if she did overhear him tell another prof that the presentation on *The Great Gatsby* she'd worked all weekend on gave just about as much evidence of an active intelligence as would the streaks left behind on a piece of paper by a moving slug.

Of course, Meredith is aware she's no genius, which is perfectly okay with her, since smart people never appear to be having a particularly good time anyway, like for instance those American lady poets Professor Donegan is so wild about, who stuck their heads into the oven and so forth, just because some male poet or other left them for somebody else. Honestly. Talk about a lack of self-respect.

The entry under Meredith's graduation photograph in her high-school yearbook read, "A friendly smile, a friendly laugh, a friendly girl", an inscription she shared with thirteen other girls in the class. If things fail to progress with Professor Donegan, she'd like to eventually marry a man in insurance. Next to her mother, the woman she most admires is Mila Mulroney, although the Princess of Wales has better clothes.

One-and-a-half-Way Communication: An Intermediate Step

Sociable and informative as the bumper sticker has been demonstrated to be, it is nevertheless very much a one-way communication between one's car and the rest of the world. As human beings become less tentative in the area of talking to strangers, some find themselves craving a type of contact with the world at large that permits a higher degree of interraction.

Not yet ready for the heady give-and-talk of a two-way conversational exchange, but still bursting with opinions in need of expression, such individuals gravitate naturally toward the type of occupations that will put them into daily proximity with strangers who can be addressed without fear that they will impede the flow of monologue by answering back.

In the United States, cab-driving is one such popular profession, highly attractive to those of strong political conviction (often of the sort exemplified by the opinion that extra-terrestrials not only are among us, but are representing certain congressional districts of the Eastern Seaboard region).

Canada, on the other hand, has so far failed to lure the real certifiable fanatics away from the microphones of late-night radio shows and into the taxi ranks of the nation, perhaps as a by-product of our general inability to inspire our citizenry to rabid conviction about anything, except possibly the incontestable superiority of tire chains over tire studs.

Of course, whatever country you live in, dentists are notorious practitioners of the one-and-a-half-way conversation. We are all of us far too accustomed to being motioned into the chair by a macabrely silent figure whose conversational skills appear to have been learned from viewing horror films featuring characters called Igor. However, once the draining-hook, drill, and various other apparati are firmly in place in our mouths, this erstwhile master of mime suddenly turns into Chatty Cathy and accosts us with open-ended questions like, "So where do you think the Jays are going to pick up a good reliever from?"

But what seems even more puzzling, not to mention downright disquieting, is the tendency of many dentists to wait until the patient's mouth is thus encumbered before making not only polite conversation, but also really vital inquiries, such as: "Have I explained to you that I don't believe in Novocain?", "How serious would a facial disfigurement be to your work?", and "I think anybody can become a qualified oral surgeon by studying at home, don't you?"

Two-Way Communication: Now You're Talking!

Ultimately, though, when you're talking inter-stranger communication, you're really talking a two-way exchange, of the type that is only achieved by certain skilful individuals at specified times in designated localities. Or to be precise, the kind of conversation between strangers that is conducted by women readjusting their makeup in front of a washroom mirror in a restaurant.

You will notice that I have specified the washroom in a restaurant, and believe me, I have good reason for doing so. While it's true that women have a propensity to talk freely and comfortably to each other in public washrooms of almost any kind, it is in restaurant ladies' rooms that the level of conversation could be truly said to approach high art.

In bus and train stations, on the other hand, the talk tends to be of an extremely utilitarian sort, centring as it so often does on the cruel injustices of a system that requires payment of a dime before women can perform a function most look upon as a necessary bore, rather than as the exercising of a consumer option.

In this situation, someone in the group can always be counted upon to reiterate that old feminist wheeze to the effect that if God had meant there to be pay toilets, we would all have been born with correct change. Otherwise, little communication of any substance occurs, apart from the few words of direction necessary to ensure that each woman emerging from the cubicle remembers to hold the door open for the next occupant, so that the insertion of a fresh dime will not be required.

So effective has this door-holding technique proved over time, in fact, that a Department of Highways survey done of the bus terminal in Holdfast, Saskatchewan, determined that the same dime has been operating the cubicle in the women's washroom there since 1946.

The women's bathrooms of movie theatres (often inexplicably referred to as "the ladies' lounge", although lining up with three hundred other women in front of two cubicles marked "Out of Order" eight minutes before the feature presentation is due to begin tallies with few women's idea of truly lounging) do not boast a particularly elevated level of stranger-talk either.

For one thing, women tend to enter cinema restrooms in clannish groups, and therefore are not particularly interested in making new friends. Considering what most women can be overheard to say to each other on these occasions, it is just as well, really, that one does not attempt to go shopping for companionship amongst one's fellow movie patrons.

"I don't understand. What did they have to go and kill each other for?"

"It was him. He was crazy. On account of being Jewish or something."

"Come on, Meryl Streep was the Jewish one. You could tell when they cut her hair all short and like that."

"No way. She *wanted* her hair like that, dumbo. Like, it's about her choice, right?"

Now, in a restaurant ladies' room, there is no danger of encountering anything like the foregoing. The reason being that women do not flock to restaurant washrooms in groups; nor do they proceed there primarily to attend to the demands of nature. Instead, women go to the washroom in a restaurant in order to get away from the old college buddy from Cleveland who has been reminiscing with their husband nonstop for the past hour and a half; they go there to make new acquaintances, to borrow some fresh cologne, and to have their morale boosted by a sympathetic stranger.

The whole thing, in fact, is like some sort of superannuated slumber party, and any girl can get in on the fun. All you need to do is swoop up to a mirror, tweak at a lock of your hair, and pronounce the word "Ugh" in a tone of profound dissatisfaction. Whereupon the woman at the mirror to your right will pause in mid-comb, smile at you compassionately, and say, "Boy, do I know the feeling. *My* husband's old roomie from Bishop's came along."

From that point you're off – trading recipes, debating what color of shadow goes best with grey eyes, recalling how much better the pressed duck was before the restaurant changed hands, and discussing the seemingly inevitable ghastliness of spouses' old university associates. In fact, it's with much reluctance, and perhaps even a fugitive tear, that you eventually realize it's time to pry yourself away from your charming companion and return to the table, where, no doubt, conflicting versions of the old fraternity handshake are being demonstrated and argued over.

Dollars to doughnuts, as you are slipping unobtrusively back into your chair, and already missing the woman you met in the bathroom more than you can say, your husband will turn to you and say, "Well, finally! What the heck do you women *do* in there, anyway?"

By now, the observant reader will have noticed that I am very careful, always, to stipulate that what I refer to here is *women* talking to *female* strangers in *ladies'* restrooms. None of the above applies to men in any public men's room, for the very good reason that men make it an ironclad policy never to talk to strangers in the washroom.

For one thing, they prefer to save their life-stories for women with whom they are trying to score. For another, they are afraid that striking up a conversation with the person at the next urinal will give the impression that they are on the make. Besides which, they are already convinced that the person at the next urinal *is* on the make.

This being the case, it has long been a puzzle to sociologists why women are the ones who insist on private cubicles in their washrooms, since they never seem to worry if the woman at the next mirror is on the make – only if she has a shot of decent cologne she might be willing to part with.

Catcher in the Rye-and-Water

Modern Literature. Some racket. Otherwise, there's not much you can say about it, except that it's full of surprises. So when Clancy, the departmental secretary, poked her head into my office, I figured something was up.

"Something's up," said Clancy, confirming my hunch. "There's a Mrs. Stradlater to see you."

Good old Clancy. Always straight to the point. Nothing to write home about in the looks department, but word-wise, she's as concise as the *Shorter Oxford*.

"Mrs. Stradlater?" I shot back. "Never heard of her." And I hadn't. No point trying to bluff Clancy. Clancy knows me like a book – *The Carpetbaggers*, to be exact. It's the only book Clancy's ever made it through.

"Look," said Clancy, "you wanna see her or not?"

Some days, it makes better sense not to get out of bed. Some days, no matter which way you jump, you can wind up in alleys blinder than John Milton in a darkroom. It was about to turn into one of those days, only I didn't know it yet. I told Clancy to show the Stradlater woman in.

To describe Mrs. Stradlater as a well-preserved dame in her forties would be to sell her short. She was in mint condition, like a well-bound set of Thackeray, and she had that restless quality you find in women with too much time on their manicured hands and too much dough in their Hermès handbags. Still, there was something about her I liked. Maybe it was the way she crossed her legs when she sat down. Or maybe it was the crisp C-note she crossed my palm with as soon as her legs were arranged.

"What's this for?" I asked, playing for time.

"There's a man I'm trying to find," said Mrs. Stradlater. "I have reason to believe he's up in Canada."

Obviously she was an American. Who else would use the expression "up in Canada"? A Greenlander would have said "down in Canada". In my business, you get so you pick up on little things like that.

"Lady, you lost somebody, go talk to the cops. I've got term papers to grade."

"Oh no." Mrs. Stradlater exhaled smoke through her well-shaped nostrils. Quite a trick, considering she didn't have a cigarette. "*You* are the only person who can find him for me. Professor – don't you recognize me?"

There *was* something familiar about her – damned if I knew what. Something that reminds you of words and images you've run into before – like a student essay cribbed from *Coles Notes*.

"Jane Stradlater," she said, when it was clear I'd drawn a blank. "I used to be Jane Gallagher. Before Ward Stradlater and I got married."

Jane Gallagher! It was as hard to swallow as the ending of an O. Henry story. But I knew she was on the level. Under the furs and the Elizabeth Arden face, it was little Jane Gallagher all right. Much older of course, but then, who isn't?

"Jane Gallagher," I said. "From *The Catcher in the Rye*. The girl Holden Caulfield really loved, but never phoned. The girl who used to keep all her kings in the back row. The girl – " I tried to stop myself, but Jane was too fast for me.

"The girl Ward Stradlater gave the time to, in the back of a car," she said evenly. "Yes, that's me. After Ward knocked me up, I married him. That's what girls did in those days. We've been married for over thirty years, but I've loved Holden Caulfield all this time. That's why you've got to find him for me, Professor."

"Stop calling me Professor. I'm only a sessional lecturer." It was the only comeback I could think of to her crazy proposition.

Jane Gallagher glanced around my office, and took in the

battered desk, the torn blind, and the dented waste can. "Okay, so you've gotten some bad academic breaks. But the way I hear it, you're a first-rate literary sleuth."

"You hear wrong, lady. I'm just a flat-footed lecturer. Strictly survey-course stuff, maybe an honors tutorial, if it comes my way. Lousy work, but someone has to do it."

Suddenly, Jane Gallagher began to sob like a baby. I'd seen dames turn on the waterworks before, but this was for real. You'd think she'd lost her stack pass the night before the orals.

"Professor," she sniffled, "you've got to help me. I can't track Holden down by myself. For one thing, when you're a fictional character, it's hard to flag a cab."

What can I say? Once a sucker, always a sucker. I told Jane Gallagher that if she stopped bawling, I'd see what I could do. I told her my fee was a century-note a day, plus expenses. I told her that even for a non-fictional character, flagging a cab in Toronto wasn't necessarily a gilt-edged proposition.

"But listen," I said, once I'd quieted her down with a slug from the bottle I keep in my desk to help me through departmental meetings, "what makes you so sure Holden Caulfield is in T.O.?"

"Just a hunch." A smile came through her tears, like the sun from behind the clouds in *The Scarlet Letter*. "His little sister Phoebe moved up here years ago with a draft-dodger. And you know how close Holden was to his sister."

I knew all right. I'd read the book, like everybody else.

"I understand Phoebe became a writer," Jane went on. "Unfortunately, she writes under a pseudonym."

"Swell."

"Professor, if anyone can find the Caulfields, you can."

"Listen," I cracked, "as far as I'm concerned, you're backing the wrong horse. But it's your dough at the wicket."

"That's right. And I have every confidence."

I wanted to share that confidence. After I'd ushered Jane Gallagher out of my office and poured myself another shot, I buzzed Clancy and told her to hold my calls.

"What calls?" Clancy wanted to know.

It was a good question. The best one I'd heard all day, in fact.

"So how did you track me down?" asked Phoebe Caulfield.

"Lucky shot." Not strictly true, but I saw no point in telling her there's an elementary rule in research: when in doubt, return to your primary source. I'd thumbed my dog-eared copy of *The Catcher in the Rye* and noted how Phoebe had called herself Hazel Weatherfield as a child. You didn't have to be *summa cum laude* to figure that the adult Phoebe would cop the same alias.

And how good the literary life had been to Hazel Weatherfield, née Phoebe Caulfield. Her sky-scraping suite in the ManuLife Centre and the designer jogging togs draping her svelte form gave impressive testimony to the fact that heartaching Harlequin romances pay nicer dividends than articles in *The University of Toronto Quarterly*. Some world. But I guess I'd known that, even before I'd rung Phoebe's chimes and felt the cold kiss of the glass of kir she pressed into my hand.

"My brother doesn't like snoops," she said with a toss of her hair, still as red as a Hardy sunset.

"So you *are* in touch with Holden?"

She smiled, but it didn't look as good on her as it did on Jane Gallagher. "I don't like snoops myself. Why don't you drink your kir like a good boy and run along?"

I never did go for taking my cues from skirts. Not even skirts in velour sweatpants. So, instead, I jerked my head toward the pricey pine bookcase, loaded down with Harlequin titles.

"Seems you've done pretty well for yourself in the frozen North. For a poor little rich girl whose hubby beat the draft."

She followed my glance to the bookcase, and took in all the "by Hazel Weatherfield" volumes as if she'd never seen them before. "A girl's got to live," she shrugged. "My husband ran out a long time ago."

"Divorce? No kidding? Now, divorce is something that seldom crops up in Harlequin books."

"Mister, you've got too damn much to say."

"So my students tell me. But some of it helps them pass their exams."

She didn't have an answer for that. Instead, she got up nervously and put a disc on the stereo. "Little Shirley Beans" was the tune. I recalled the page in the book where Holden bought her that record. So Phoebe had a sentimental streak, under all the expensive decor. It didn't surprise me. You compile the kind of *curriculum vitae* I'd compiled, nothing much surprises you any more.

"Cut the stall, Phoebe. Holden Caulfield's in Toronto, and you know where."

She looked at me pleadingly, and for a second I saw the sweet little girl from thirty-years-and-change before. "Holden doesn't see people. You've got to understand, mister. He was a symbol to an entire generation. That kind of responsibility – it's too much for anyone."

I understood all right. You can't read *Lord Jim* and not get the straight dope on responsibility. Still, I had a job to do. In spite of this little mouse who cranked out trashy romances and cried big crocodile tears into her kir over her highly symbolic brother, while the band played "Little Shirley Beans".

"Tell me where to find him, Phoebe."

"Let yourself out," Phoebe rapped. "I've got to get changed for an appointment with my therapist."

As the record came to a scratchy stop, she rushed out of the room so fast, you would have thought Hart Crane first editions were on sale in the bedroom. Which left me to listen to the thump of the phonograph needle while I stared up at the bookshelves. Suddenly I noticed that, next to all the "Hazel Weatherfield" Harlequins, there was a bound manuscript. A screenplay, by the look of it. *Random Harvest II*, by Rudolf Schmidt.

Who the hell would remake *Random Harvest*? And who the hell was Rudolf Schmidt? I felt icy fingers of familiarity walk up my spine – the same fingers Jane Stradlater's arrival in my office had set in motion. For once, I decided to take my cues from a skirt after all. I tossed off my kir like a good boy, let myself out, and ran along – just the way Phoebe Caulfield had wanted it.

The Twenty-Two was crowded as usual, and as murky as the prose style of Theodore Dreiser. Still, I had no trouble spotting a likely prospect at a table near the bar. You don't see many red hunting hats in fashionable Toronto watering-holes. Lots of down-filled vests, but very few hunting hats.

I approached his table with a large spritzer and a larger smile. "Excuse me, but aren't you Rudolf Schmidt?"

He looked up from his rye-and-water in surprise. "How'd you know?"

"Lucky shot," I said, pulling up a chair. "I'm crazy about the remake of *Random Harvest* you wrote, and I figured The Twenty-Two was a likely spot to find a screenwriter."

He was eyeing me suspiciously. "Say, this isn't some weird kind of flitty pass, is it? Because I *hate* that kind of stuff, if you want to know the truth. I really do."

It certainly sounded like Caulfield. Sure, he'd gained weight over the years, and his hair was entirely grey now, but everything else was checking out.

"Nothing like that," I assured him. "It's just that when a piece of writing really knocks me out, I find myself wishing I could call up the author and tell him so. You know the feeling?"

Bull's-eye, I thought, as his pupils dilated wide. It was Caulfield all right, and he was wondering if I was on to him.

"You're a prince," he said. "You really are, no kidding. But I gotta go." He stood up and fished some crumpled bills from his pocket to cover the tab.

"What's your hurry, Rudolf?"

"I hate this place like poison, if you want to know. The phonies are coming in the goddam windows."

"Right," I agreed smoothly. "Myself, I prefer to go to Riverdale Farm and watch the animals. Only I wonder, Rudolf – where do the ducks go in the winter?"

He froze right up, his hand still stuck in his pocket. "How'd you guess it was me?"

"Rudolf Schmidt was the fake name you used in the book."

"God, I *knew* I should of come up with a new one. I'm a real moron sometimes, you know that?"

"But the *Random Harvest II* project was the real giveaway. You talked a lot about the original *Random Harvest* in the book."

"But I never gave the title. Boy, the plot *alone* was enough to make you puke."

"Right, you hated that film. In fact, you hated all movies, didn't you? But now you're writing screenplays and schmoozing with media types at The Twenty-Two. How could you do this to your fans, Holden? You, of all people?"

He pulled the peak of the red hunting hat over his eyes, and for a second I worried I'd gone too far. But when he spoke, his voice was calm.

"Look, it's not like I didn't try to keep my public from finding

out and all. I mean, I changed my goddam *name*, right? And I took
the trouble to move up to Toronto. I figured if I was gonna sell
out, at least I'd do it in a place where nobody would find *out* about
it."

He had a point there. I had to admit it.

"Besides," he went on, "you think *I'm* the only literary figure in
the whole world who turned out to be a phony and came here to
keep it quiet? Take a look around, buddy. See that old guy shootin'
the old bull to the thin air? That's good old Sydney Carton, from *A
Tale of Two Cities*. He never went to the guillotine for old Charles
Darnay. In the end, he chickened out. So now all he does is, he
hangs around here mumbling to himself, 'It's a far far better
Scotch I drink than I have ever drunk.' And you see that loaded-
looking blonde, giving all the men the old eye? Nora, from Ibsen's
A Doll's House. Old Nora's made a killing in the chocolate maca-
roon business, she really has. But she can't find herself a man who
isn't intimidated by her success. And then there's – "

"Knock it off," I barked. I didn't want to hear any more.

"It happens, buddy," Caulfield said. "To everybody. I mean,
just because a person happens to be *fictional*, it doesn't make
him – wuddayacallit – immune."

"Yeah? You tell that to Jane Gallagher. She still keeps her kings
in the back row for you."

"Jane!" The color drained from his face. "You've seen her?"

"She's the one who hired me to find you. She wants it back,
Holden. The way it used to be."

"Look, old buddy – old buddyroo." He was on his feet and
babbling incoherently like a Ginsberg poem. "I can't see her. I'm
just – not in the mood, y'know? And don't tell her how I turned
out. It'll kill her. It really will."

And he was gone. For a second, I debated going after him, but
only for a second. What was the point? Jane Gallagher could keep
her C-notes and her luscious smile. I was off the case, as of now. I
took one last look around the bar, and spotted Rhett Butler
putting the make on some waiter, telling the kid that, frankly, he
did give a damn.

I paid for my spritzer and left The Twenty-Two, feeling as blue
as a remaindered copy of *The Lower Depths*. Some town, Toronto, I
thought. Some racket, literature.

On my way home, I stopped off at a newsstand and bought the latest *National Enquirer*, with Johnny and Joanna Carson on the front page and a story about carcinogenic UFOs inside. Let's hear it for real life, I thought. From now on, I was keeping my nose strictly out of good books. Real life has one big plus – it doesn't get your hopes up.

Guilt

Some time ago, I received a polite mailing from my credit card company, informing me that a user fee would soon be charged on credit transactions involving the card. The reason for this change in policy was explained as follows: "Many customers pay their accounts in full each month and thus have not carried any of the increased servicing costs."

I must say I admired their crust. Under no circumstances was the company going to be bullied into a position of accepting responsibility for this regrettable but necessary development. Instead, the blame was being placed squarely where it belonged – on the scrawny shoulders of the overly conscientious consumer whose prompt paying habits had created the problem in the first place.

Yessiree, I thought, humming purposefully as I snipped the plastic card into several pieces and force-fed them to the guppy. Here was yet another glittering example of the many constructive uses of Guilt.

Guilt, as you probably know, is big business. And nowhere is the trading in guilt-edged insecurities brisker than right here in Canada.

Now, steady on there a minute, I hear you saying. What about the Germans? Don't they lead the world in guilt production? And let's not forget about the Americans, who managed to agonize their way through a civil war, the bombing of Hiroshima, and the invasion of Vietnam in the same length of time it took Canadians to sign up for Confederation and pick a flag. Now, surely the Americans have a much larger stockpile of guilt than Canadians do.

You'd think so, but apparently not.

I was pretty surprised, myself, when I completed my research and tabulated my findings on the subject, to discover that Canada has probably the world's largest untapped supply of guilt. If you're still unconvinced, allow me to share with you some of the highlights of my exploration of this rich field.

Sources of Guilt: The Old, Middle, and New Kingdoms

In the sixties, God said, "Let there be Guilt," to which the civil rights activists and war protesters replied, "Right on!"

Of course, in this country, the issue of moral responsibility was slightly complicated by the fact that we just didn't *feel* all that morally responsible, somehow, for the lousy state of the world. After all, Canadians weren't the ones flambé-ing churches in Alabama, or playing Sink the Sub in the Gulf of Tonkin, right?

Consequently, it was with a certain amount of understandable confusion that we chanted, "We shall overcome," and "Hell no, we won't go." Overcome what? Go where?

My God, we began to think nervously, is it marginally possible that we're out here shouting, "Hey, hey, LBJ, how many kids did you kill today?" only because we can't think of a rhyme for Pearson? I mean, what kind of people does that make us, anyway? Coattailing on other people's crises just because we don't have a government that's sufficiently together to murder the cream of the country's youth. How low can you get?

It was in attempting to grope toward an answer to that question, and many others, that we lost our collective footing, and stumbled instead upon the mother lode of Canadian guilt.

In the Middle Period of the Guilted Age – the 1970s – social causes were largely replaced by a rabid and earnest contemplation of the self. Nevertheless, the so-called Me Generation was still able to make time to feel guilty about its self-absorption, and once more Canadians were soon able to take a commanding lead, with significant pioneering work in the concept of Feeling Guilty About Feeling Guilty.

The fact that the best-selling self-help book of the period, *If I'm My Own Best Friend, Why Can't I Feel Okay About Looking Out For Number One?*, was written by an American and published in the States only assisted conscience-stricken Canadian nationalists in their never-ending quest for ultimate self-castigation.

The advent of the 1980s, however, saw a whole new development in the Canadian Guilt industry, in the form of the No-Win Situation, which, as observant students of guilt have pointed out, is really a refinement of the Middle Period's guilt-for-guilt's-sake syndrome writ large.

The No-Win Situation is best exemplified by the dilemma of a man who begins by feeling guilty about being out of shape, and tries to take up jogging to rectify the problem – only to end up feeling even more guilty when he learns that jogging may be as bad for him as obesity.

For such a person, no alternative provides any relief. Noontime racquetball makes him feel guilty as he flaunts his dufflebag and racquet under the nose of his secretary, typing reports on her lunch-hour. Dieting reminds him uneasily of the starving millions for whom slimming cannot be construed as an option.

He could, of course, solve his weight problem by taking up smoking. Or could he?

Social Uses of Guilt

Nowhere else in Canada has guilt proved its value as a natural resource so dramatically as it has in the bullying and intimidation of smokers.

At one time during the 1970s, it was considered necessary to create no-smoking zones in public buildings, restaurants, and movie theatres in order to impress upon smokers that their kind wasn't wanted here.

Now, however, guilt alone can do the trick. Verify this by observing the action at the next party you go to, where you will notice the few smokers huddled in secluded corners like hunted things, pursuing their lonely depravity.

Fine and dandy. That is, of course, as it should be in a society that is so guilt-oriented that the government spends the millions that it reaps in tobacco taxes on advertising campaigns that flagellate us about the dangers of smoking.

But where guilt really comes to a finely honed point in the smoking issue is the clever way in which the smokers at parties are manipulated into assuaging their guilt by accommodating a steady stream of *schnorrers*, who intrude upon their Molokai-like seclusion in order to bum a smoke because they "still enjoy one with a drink".

For their part, economists have begun to puzzle over the mathematical fragility of a supply-and-demand situation in which everybody appears to be smoking, while hardly anyone seems to actually buy any more. The centre, they have warned us time and again, cannot possibly hold – and then to allay their apprehensions, they promptly beg us to spot them a cigarette.

Distribution of Guilt by Regions

Guilt can be found in great abundance in almost every province of Canada. But then, such a widespread distribution is hardly surprising in a nation whose motto speaks movingly of the onerous responsibility of ensuring that the shoreline of the country continues to meet the ocean on either side; a nation whose anthem rashly pledges the citizenry to stand endlessly on guard, but never once intimates against *what*; a nation whose long-standing Prime Minister gave new meaning to the phrase "responsible government" by carefully explaining to us time and again that the state of the economy was really our fault.

However, there are certain areas of Canada in which guilt can be found in particularly rich concentrations, and it is important for us to understand how this circumstance has come about.

Central Canada – otherwise known as Ontario – is enormously well-endowed with guilt, especially in its southern regions, where the city of Toronto is generally known as "Canada's Guilt Capital", and features a tall, tower-like monument that is, in fact, in the shape of the world's tallest free-standing nail, as a symbol of how willingly Toronto has impaled itself on the sins of the rest of the country.

Guilt in Toronto is available in quantity on almost every downtown street, where citizens can be heard remarking to each other that the current bad weather must be payment for the lovely summer the year before, and exhorting their friends to "Take care, eh?" (which phrase, etymologists tell us, is merely a colloquial derivative of the more formal injunction to "Stand on guard" found in the aforementioned national anthem).

As far as the rest of the country goes, it is customary in matters pertaining to Canada to assume that the concept of regional disparity has a relevant part to play in any comparison study of one area with another. In the case of guilt, however, it is far too simplistic to hypothesize that it is the relatively affluent regions of the country that hold the monopoly on this precious substance.

To the contrary, in the Maritime provinces – designated traditionally as a have-not area – guilt has always run very high, partly as a result of a great concentration of Scottish forebears (see The Origins of Guilt, below) and partly because they got all the best lobsters.

And whatever the state of its fortunes, one of the most guilt-ridden parts of the country throughout history has always been the prairie region, especially during those Depression-era times when the area had very little going for it economically. What Alberta, Saskatchewan, and Manitoba managed to find to feel guilty about at the height of the Dust Bowl period has never been clear, except that psychologists feel there is reason to suspect a residual sense of carelessness, arising from the inexplicable misplacement of so many buffalo in the late nineteenth century.

Interestingly, the only virtually guilt-free province in Canada is Quebec, where, in spite of a strong Roman Catholic heritage, guilt has been almost totally eradicated, following an assiduous and thorough-going government campaign involving legislation to make innocence the working emotion in La Belle Province.

The Quebec experience may give rise to some uneasy speculation about the possible fate of guilt in the rest of the country. In order to reassure ourselves that this valuable substance is indeed a renewable resource, we must look closely at its origins.

Can we possibly discover where Canadian guilt comes from? Do we have any idea how it was formed? And will Canadians ever run out of this precious material? The answers to those questions are: Yes, maybe, and emphatically not.

The Origins of Guilt

Like so much else in this country, Canadian guilt was originally imported from Great Britain, particularly Scotland, whose downtrodden inhabitants swarmed eagerly to this land of promise in their grateful thousands (albeit at gunpoint) in the early part of the last century.

No one is exactly certain how the Scots got to feel so guilty in the first place, considering that they were a hard-pressed people with little that others might envy, unless others happened to have an unaccountable yen for blood pudding or chapped knees.

In the absence of other data, some historians have speculated that it may have been Calvinism that caused the Scots to feel so guilty as a people, and they point, by way of evidence, to the interesting fact that there was indeed a theologian named John Calvin whose teachings did exert enormous influence over the peoples of Northern Europe at one time.

Other scholars, however, dismiss the postulated link between Calvinism and this John Calvin person as far too tenuous to be credited, and insist instead that Calvinism was, in fact, derived from a spiritualist cult of the nineteenth century the devotees of which anticipated the sour visage of future American President Calvin Coolidge in a dream, and subsequently organized their worship around preparing themselves for Calvin's coming by learning to speak without moving their lips or making any extravagant gestures.

So much for the origins of guilt in Canada. It is now time to examine yet another vital question in the evolution of this bountiful natural resource. Namely, what were the enormous subterranean pressures that have transformed the raw material of Calvinistic guilt into the highly refined neurotic substance in the production of which our country leads the world today?

Distribution of Guilt by Sex: A Demographic Overview

As far as the conversion process by which guilt is created is concerned, sex has always been nature's perfect catalyst. Which is perhaps why experts tell us that as long as human relationships endure, so will guilt. Hence, it would seem there is no real reason to fear the coming of a day when Canadians wake up to find themselves fresh out of the emotional fuel that powers the giant turbines of remorse, entrapment, repining, and resentment that provide, in their turn, the energy source for more than ninety per cent of the human interaction in this country.

But how equal is the distribution of guilt between the sexes? Not very. Up-to-date surveys show us that in this regard, as in so many others, men have been endowed with the lion's share of a valuable resource material.

In extramarital relationships, for example, men demonstrate a striking proclivity for wallowing in regret and self-recrimination, to a degree that quickly creates fatigue and ennui in their part-time partner in debauchery. "My wife is a wonderful woman," they can be heard to say, over and over. "If she knew what I was up to, it would kill her."

Having so said, many men then proceed to go to any number of preposterous lengths to prove this lachrymose thesis by finding ways to ensure that the aforementioned wonderful woman does indeed get to know what they are up to. Surprisingly, however, intelligence regarding her husband's activities seldom kills her; more commonly, she will be heard to make extravagant state-ments about wanting to kill *him*. But not even the threat of death will deter a truly determined man from feeling guilty about philandering, and he is generally prepared to feel guilty again and again.

However, while men get to derive three-quarters of their enjoy-ment of illicit sex from the life-giving *frisson* of guilt it inspires, women have not been so lucky, and have always had to make their own fun in the adultery department. Try as they will (and they do try, believe me), women simply cannot bring themselves to feel very guilty about fooling around.

Women learn from an early age that, although the world may have short-changed them in the guilt department, they have been somewhat compensated by a generous endowment in the area of rationalization. Thus it becomes possible for any woman to justify an extra-curricular dalliance as a form of self-esteem enhance-ment absolutely vital to the well-being of her marriage and, indeed, being undertaken solely for the ultimate (if admittedly somewhat indirect) benefit of her husband.

In other areas of guilt-ridden social interaction – such as the workplace – Canadian men have also shown themselves to be miles ahead of their female counterparts. For example, a man will always be very careful to tell a female co-worker how badly he feels about earning twice as much as she does for doing the same job (sometimes even showing her his pay-cheque stub for emphasis), while most women lack the imagination and sensitivity to understand how a man could feel so poignantly about a situation he shows no apparent intention of rectifying.

Men are likewise extremely uncomfortable with the kind of ruthless tactics the cut-throat executive world often forces them to indulge in, which is the main reason they often find it necessary to linger over three-martini lunches, merely to blunt the keen edges of their remorse.

Meanwhile, their free-wheeling female employees can be found back in the office, polishing off nourishing portions of no-name cottage cheese and caffeine-reduced Tab at their comfortable desks, before ambling out of doors to enjoy the rest of an idle forty-five-minute lunch-hour picking up a birthday gift for the boss's wife, dropping off their husband's drycleaning, doing their mother's banking, and then sauntering in a leisurely way over to their son's school to exchange lighthearted speculations with the principal as to what might have inspired the child to set fire to several of his classmates.

Guilt in Nature: A Special Consideration

Although human beings tend to think of themselves as having a monopoly on the sensitive emotion under discussion, studies on less highly evolved creatures show great natural reservoirs of guilt in many familiar Canadian species.

For instance, scientists now believe that our national symbol, the beaver, is not so much busy as overwrought. He may, in fact, undertake his ambitious construction projects merely as a way of assuaging the guilt stemming from feelings of hostility and resentment at being relegated to the five-cent piece, while the comparatively low-profile caribou gets to luxuriate on the quarter.

Meanwhile, in the domain of our feathered friends, we have come to see that the number one Bird in a Guilted Cage is none other than our very own Canada Goose, as demonstrated by this creature's unwavering tendency to begin every sentence with "I'm sorry, but..."

But the most compelling evidence for the excessive guiltiness of Canadian animals over the species of other countries comes from a detailed examination made of various breeds of dogs emanating from different lands.

While the tiny Chihuahua derives ample job-satisfaction from selling garish postcards and crudely executed pottery by the roadside; while the Irish setter is happy to waste entire days in the pub telling extravagant stories; and while even the American cocker feels entitled to relax on weekends in front of the TV, Canada's own Labrador is a virtual canine workaholic.

Not content to spend a full day retrieving in the marshes, the Labrador is often found also attending evening education courses, where he learns how to become a security guard, or readies himself for the job of helping the handicapped.

The Labrador is also possessed of a highly developed social conscience, and while he has sometimes been criticized abroad for remaining dumb on human-rights issues, it must be noted that he tries to make a point of keeping himself abreast of current affairs, and shows a keen interest in newspapers from an early age.

The Future of Canadian Guilt: A Conclusion

Whither Canadian guilt? Or, to put the question another way, what should be done with our abnormally generous allotment of this valuable resource – besides just feeling guilty about it?

My own recommendation, based on the research I have undertaken, is that we seriously consider the possibility of exporting our national guilt, the logical successor to wheat.

Naturally infectious, guilt is therefore easily transported. More importantly, the psychological complexities suggested by this valuable resource promise to do much to upgrade Canada's shambling bucolic image abroad as a mere hewer of wood and drawer of you-know-what.

In fact, in contemplating a sanguine future for this country as a major guilt supplier to the world, only one consideration need sober us and continue to niggle at the back of the mind: how do we prevent the Japanese from finding a way to produce guilt better and cheaper than we can?

Careers in Crime

Generally speaking, I'm not one of those women who complain about the fact that it's a man's world. Frankly, I don't think highly enough of the world most of the time to begrudge it to them.

Besides which, when you come to look at it, all this man's-world business is based on some pretty flimsy evidence. I mean, so what if men get all the high-paying jobs, and even when they *do* do the same job as a woman, manage to get paid more for it?

Do I mind? Certainly not. After all, men have financial responsibilities that women can't even imagine. Like paying off their bookies. And hiring someone else to shine their shoes.

Of course, it's also arguable that in certain respects their lives are *less* expensive than ours are. For one thing, their cologne lasts longer. It's true. I once accidentally spilled a half-drop of Aramis on the cuff of my sweater when sample-sniffing it for my boyfriend. Six months later, while wearing the same sweater, I was accosted on the streetcar by a beautiful and amorous young woman who mistook me for Dustin Hoffman. Or perhaps it was because we have the same sloping shoulders.

At any rate, we dated for several weeks before she realized her mistake, and I remember it as a terrific interlude, except that I had to pick up the tab most of the time when we dined out. That's another financial hazard of being a man, by the way. Although I will say in the young lady's defence that she didn't mind sewing on the odd button when I asked her to, and she was touchingly willing to sit up late at night, watching reruns of *The Graduate* with me.

You also hear women complain that men, in addition to making more money, also have things easier than we do. What a lot of hooey. It's infinitely harder being a man, and I'll tell you why.

For one thing, as you will quickly realize if you tune in to beer commercials on TV, men are seldom allowed to simply walk out of a room. No. They must "cut out" or "head outa here", usually donning mirror-tinted sunglasses as they go. They are also expected to take their leave under the power of some complicated and uncomfortable vehicle like a motorcycle, snowmobile, or dune buggy.

Worse than that, the places they are inevitably cuttin' out to turn out to be soggy duck-blinds or poorly heated log cabins, populated by gangs of wise-cracking morons, lovingly referred to in the voice-over as "the boys" or "the guys". The only beverage available for general consumption is the sponsor's beer, and there's always some joker on hand who can be counted upon to pull somebody else's cap down over his eyes.

Meanwhile, the women who pertain to these galoots are presumably back in town, cosily sipping dry martinis in a good restaurant, and talking wistfully among themselves about the difficulties inherent in meeting a man who knows something about Proust.

As if that weren't bad enough, men are also the half of the population required to worry about death, since women refuse to give the subject more than a passing thought. It's men who have favorite sweaters that are continually being given away to Goodwill, either by mistake or by design, and men are the ones compelled to know where the fuse box is, and how to drink milk straight from the carton.

Being a man means, among other things, being obliged to look good in flat shoes, bold plaids, and executive-length socks. It means being addressed as "buddy" by total strangers on the street, being expected to know how to whittle, and sometimes even being required to drive a van with a shag-carpeted interior.

Men are the ones who must know how to do Joe Cocker imitations, hook up the stereo speakers, flip quarters across their knuckles, and shuffle cards properly.

True, it may be women who bear the primary responsibility in our society for birth-control, child-rearing, and remembering to take the dog for his shots, but so what? These concerns are mere bagatelles, when put up against the really weighty problems men have to contend with, like playing touch football with bad knees, and trying to find a truly effective electric razor.

For all of that, there remain two areas of human endeavor in which men still maintain such total superiority than even I am moved to something like jealousy.

One is the ability to go to the bathroom in the woods without first having to spend valuable hours hunting for a spot where the foot of man not only has never trod, but is also unlikely to do so in the next four minutes.

And the other is participation in organized crime.

Even in docile Canada, what the newscasters refer to as "mob-related crime" has become such a prominent fact of life that it is no longer necessary for a young Canadian to put on ice skates and carry a hockey stick in order for the darker side of his nature to emerge. Now, all that is required to bring out his blacker impulses is a video cassette of *The Godfather* and an uncle in the construction business.

You'd think, just offhand, that if Canadians as a group are beginning to make noticeable inroads into this burgeoning career field, women ought to be right there in the vanguard of violence and corruption.

After all, this is a country that places a high priority on equal job opportunities for women, to the extent that of the close to three hundred Members of Parliament sitting (and I mean sitting) in Ottawa, almost a handful are women. While in the token clutch of Canadians chosen to participate in NASA's astronaut program, one is actually a token woman.

However, breaking into the domain of organized crime presents women with problems far less surmountable than those posed by entering comparatively more accessible professions, like pimping, or the Catholic priesthood.

The main stumbling-block has been the male gangster establishment itself, to whom the concept of "affirmative action" is meaningless, unless it refers to machine-gunning someone while he is in the act of saying "yes", and for whom the idea of a God*mother* applies only to the woman who provided a fancy-dress wardrobe to Cinderella.

So, to a great extent, the role of women in gangland has remained a very limited one indeed, and consists mainly of stirring veal-and-peppers in the kitchen, while in the dining room the men divide up territories for heroin distribution. As a rule, in fact, mob-related women only get out of the kitchen to attend the occasional funeral.

Otherwise, women have been singularly unsuccessful in penetrating the inner circles of male mobsterdom, except of course, as "molls". But to a modern woman, the notion of spending her time doing what a moll is expected to do – buffing her nails, snapping her gum, and demanding in a high-pitched voice to be taken out to nightclubs – hardly suggests a pertinent use of her talents, as not even minimal secretarial skills are required.

Besides which, in the gun-moll game, one's status is very closely linked to that of one's steady escort. To the point that if your boyfriend inexplicably turns up one day as part of the infrastructure of an expressway collector lane, it's highly advisable for you to suddenly remember a pressing engagement in Sierra Leone.

Consequently, it's become more and more fashionable for ambitious women with a yen for adventure to bypass the traditional wife-and-gun-moll routes to organized crime, and to start contemplating methods of ingress into rackets of their very own.

And why not? Gangster life offers a number of attractive perquisites to any enterprising woman. First, there are the large, sleek cars, and with a wheelman of your own, parking is never a problem. Secondly, you have the promise of a busy social life, since much gangland business is conducted in a relaxed and gossipy way over a pasta lunch in a restaurant.

Worried about calories? You needn't be. Pinstripes are marvellously slimming.

Best of all, the mob is a terrific place to meet broad-shouldered laconic men named "Bugs", with lots of chest-hair and few opinions. Although it's wise not to become too emotionally attached, for reasons that were touched on in the segment above dealing with molls.

Nevertheless, as I've said, it's necessary to remember, when considering this appealing career, that men have been, to a great degree, extremely successful in keeping women out of the back alleys of power. Which is why, when choosing a racket for herself, a woman should avoid any of the old sentimental favorites like gambling, extortion, and narcotics.

Well, what's left, you ask? Plenty, actually. The real trick, in embarking upon a life of organized crime, is to light on an area of goods or services that a large segment of society is willing to pay dearly for, but is not willing or able to supply for themselves. After all, a gangster is essentially someone who undertakes to perform others' dirty work for a fee.

When it's put that way, I'm sure it immediately becomes obvious to you what area of criminal activity women can readily specialize in. Housework. That's right, housework. Male gangsters don't control it; everyone needs it; and if it isn't dirty work, then I don't know what is.

What I'm talking about, of course, is nothing more or less than the advent of Organized Grime – a lawless ring of such unsavory dimensions that it will soon reach right round the bathtub, and thence to the collars of the entire nation.

Now, you may be disappointed to hear that your best shot at being a *capo dei tutti capi* is in a mundane and unglamorous profession that you associate with downtrodden women in ads who can't seem to get their brights really bright, or prevent yellow waxy buildup. But let me hasten to assure you, criminality is what you make of it.

Already, in fact, there are emerging gangs of housework desperadoes – known to the police as mopsters – who have begun to extort payment for their cleaning services, and who punish the unwilling by arranging "accidents" on freshly polished floors, or by "inadvertently" dumping bleach into the washing machine that contains the colored wash of their victims.

Lest you think that intimidation of this sort is too insignificant to constitute a major law-enforcement problem, I must tell you that the police don't agree. As much as anyone else, the cop on the beat requires freshly washed and lightly pressed clothing to wear to work, and the prospect of seeing this invaluable service fall into the hands of a criminal element has sent policemen from coast to coast into a swivet.

Furthermore, I happen to know that various metropolitan

police squads in Toronto took a keen interest in a lunch meeting that was held recently in a local restaurant and attended by three major organized grime figures from across the country.

From Montreal came the notorious Madame Nette, known as the Donna of Detergents, who controls all soap trafficking across Canada. Police believe that, if crossed, Madame Nette could put the entire country on rinse cycle, permanently.

The West Coast was represented by Vancouver's vicious Jane "Rugsy" O'Halloran, the Scatter Rug Queen, who specializes in the shakedown, and the meeting took place on the home turf of Toronto's own notorious Wilma the Waxer, a remorseless killer whose victims traditionally die in a spray of Endust.

Although nobody knows the totality of what was discussed by these three key overladies (a police bugging device taped to a leg of the table was unexpectedly dislodged by Wilma the Waxer when she launched into her compulsive practice of Lemon Pledging the furniture during the dessert course), it is generally believed that the conversation centred around the touchy question of which of them would control heavy cleaning in the Maritimes.

Rugsy insisted on autonomous authority over all carpets, while Madame Nette insisted that machine-washable throw rugs rightfully belonged in her domain. Then Wilma made an unexpected power play for draperies and linens. However, none of the three expressed any interest in doing windows.

While the growing threat of nation-wide germ warfare amongst these queen-pins of grime has police worried, I myself have to admit to a real sense of pride in my enterprising gangland sisters, who are making every effort to close the gender gap by proving that brutality, deceit, and overweening greed are not innate sexual characteristics peculiar to men.

Now, all that remains is for some ingenious woman to tackle that other – er – problem. You know. . . that little matter of taking care of business in the woods?

Purse-onally Speaking

Years ago, I remember seeing a play so excruciating in its pretensions that the lead character actually referred to her purse as "the satchel of my womanhood".

Well, my theatre companions and I had a derisive hoot over that one, and for the next few weeks could count on crippling each other with mirth merely by alluding to the line. "Let me get my wallet out of the satchel of my womanhood," we would say. Or "You can't make a silk satchel of your womanhood out of a sow's ear."

Mercifully, the jokes soon faded, as did the memory of the play. But somehow that overwrought phrase stayed in my mind, and I've got to admit my respect for it has increased with age.

Because if there's one thing that women – Playboy bunnies and angry feminists alike – can definitely agree on, it's the centrality of purses. In spite of all the tasteless gags that have ever been concocted around the concept of a woman rummaging in a junk-laden handbag for her keys, most of us take this accessory very seriously indeed.

First of all, to *call* a purse an "accessory" is to sell it short. Shoes are accessories; a coral bracelet is an accessory. Even a husband can be classified as such. A purse, on the other hand, is a vital tool of the female trade.

Witness the sense of occasion most of us attach to the process of buying one. No gun-for-hire ever approached the weapons counter so professionally, or balanced the instrument as thoughtfully in his hand, or sighted down the barrel with more knowledgeable cunning than a woman assessing the relative merits of a rack of purses at Eaton's.

Is it ample enough? Can I live with mauve? What about this canvas number? Is it going to shred to pieces or what? These are only some of the key questions to be answered. And of course there are as many theories about what constitutes the Perfect Purse as there are women.

"Compartments," my friend Beverly declares without hesitation. "There have to be at least three separate compartments, one of them plastic-lined for makeup."

Myself, I've had nothing but grief with compartments, which only, as far as I'm concerned, provide the *illusion* of organization. When I buy a compartmentalized purse, I start out with the best intentions in the world – wallet and keys in one slot, cosmetics in the next, glasses and notebook in the next, and so on.

What happens, in a matter of moments, is that the keys wind up in the money compartment, the glasses somehow get smeared with mascara, and I'm thrown into a panic because my wallet has disappeared, only to resurface where the notebook was supposed to be. As for the notebook, it's *still* missing, which is too bad, since all my notes for this essay were in it.

For people like me, it makes much more sense to just bite the bullet and heave everything into one capacious pouch. Even then, however, the purse-onal decisions are only beginning.

What about the strap? How long should it be? And must it be adjustable?

"Strap? Who needs it?" sneers my friend Maureen. "Any woman worthy of the name prefers a clutch."

Maureen, I couldn't disagree more. No self-respecting purse lacks a strap – and the longer the better. I mean, I just don't feel *balanced* without a weighty shoulder-bag hanging down my right side. In those rare moments when I'm without it – in the shower for example, but even then not always – I have a definite list to the left.

And as for venturing out in public without first strapping my purse securely to my person like a bodypack – well, I'd as soon risk schussing down Mount Norquay on skis with no bindings.

But then, Maureen and I have a totally different philosophy of life, as a rapid survey of the contents of our respective reticules will reveal. Maureen is the kind of woman who when asked for a Kleenex can produce one instantly, snowy clean and neatly folded, from her little clutch.

Never in my life have I ever had a fresh Kleenex to hand over to anyone. I can proffer a mangled stick of Trident, or a soiled program from the 1969 production of *Hair*. The broken lace of a tennis shoe? How about an Air Canada swizzle stick? No problem. But a Kleenex? Don't ask.

Now, I regard this as a failing, I really do. A failure of femininity, as well as the probable explanation for my inability to get into the graduate school of my choice.

Although Maureen, I could argue in my own defence, has nothing to show for herself *except* neatly folded Kleenexes (Kleenices?). Along with a rat-tail comb. And a Buxton billfold. That's it. Those are the entire contents of her purse. Which of us is consequently the better human being, I leave to you to decide.

Of course, such a sophisticated discussion as the foregoing is totally lost on men. Men know nothing from purses and want to keep it that way, in spite of the fashion industry's recent efforts to masculate the handbag. Male resistance has, I think, less to do with their fears of effeminacy than with their genuine inability to see the purse as an identi-kit.

See, men have this quaint notion of decentralization – the idea that you stow your possessions in whatever location proves the handiest over time. Wallet in the breast pocket, comb at the hip, and for personal papers they've come up with something they call an "attaché case", which means it's clumsy to carry and trips people on the bus.

Women prefer to consolidate, to combine the trivial (lipstick) with the crucial (lipstick), and to intersperse articles of personal expression, such as a small headless teddy bear, with more banal necessities, like cash.

With the result that, for each of us, our purse is an individual creation so revealing of its owner that if we were offered the choice of telling everything about ourselves under sodium pentothal on nationwide TV, or having our purses rifled by a ham-fisted customs official, most of us would be hard put to decide which constituted the more vulgar invasion of our privacy.

Such is the power of the female purse, and if I could just lay my hands on that notebook, I'd pen a paean in its praise that would knock your socks off. As it is, however, I'm going to have to content myself with a comment my friend Dora made, when I asked her for her thoughts about purses.

"Promise not to laugh," said Dora shyly. "But more and more, I've come to think of my purse as...well, as the satchel of my womanhood."

Laugh? Me? Hey, Dora, no way.

Laurie Chesterfield's Letters to Her Sister

September 10

Dear Little Sister:

It seems awfully funny to be writing to you at Peggy's address....I guess I still can't get used to the idea of my baby sister on her own in the big wicked city type of thing....

Or maybe what's even harder to get used to is the fact that *I'm* not in the city any more, breathing that scuzzy air, getting my new coat splashed by inconsiderate drivers, sidestepping dog-doody, etc.

As you can gather, I really don't miss it a bit and only wish I'd made up my mind to move out to the country years ago. This place is fantastic, it really is. I don't know why nobody's thought of a combination ashram and discount sweater outlet before, but then maybe a genius like our spiritual leader Donny only comes along every few generations.

Anyway, here I am, happily recuperating from all those years of the swinging single life in the big town, and there you are, freshly arrived on the scene and ready to make all the same mistakes your big sister made, plus a few more of your very own, right?

Wrong. At least, I hope you're not. Maybe it's my justification for some of the grimmer experiences I had as an urban working girl, but I find myself thinking that there would be more value in all that I learned and the various ways I learned it, if it meant I was able to pass a little knowledge on to you before the fact, so to speak.

Now, I know exactly what you're thinking. "Oh boy, here we go. The heavy-duty big-sister act."

Not at all. You know me, coming on with the stern lectures isn't my style. But I know you won't be crashing at Peggy's long (if the mouth-breathing doesn't get you, the smell of that goddamn penguin or whatever it is in the cage will), and pretty soon you'll be heading out on your own, in which case maybe you can do with some friendly advice. If not, just tear this letter up unopened, or feed it to the penguin, right?

Okay, so strictly in the spirit of for-what-it's-worth, let me start off by saying something I meant to say but never got the chance last time I saw you at Mom's and Dad's, before you moved up to the city in the first place: the biggest problem you're going to run into, bar none, is men.

Now, maybe it's encouraging to hear that you're at least going to be running into some, particularly if you've been hearing all those rumors about how there aren't enough to go around.

Well, as far as I'm concerned, the amazing thing about men is how they can be so scarce and still manage to dominate every aspect of your life. It must be something they taught them in Shop, while all us girls were off in Home Ec learning how to fold raisins into the batter, right?

Anyway, men are the major concern, and the subject of my letter today. So listen up; you never know, you might learn something. First thing to be aware of is that men come in two varieties: single, and single-at-heart (otherwise known as Married But Still Hoping).

Right about now, you're probably expecting to hear that the MBSHs are the ones to avoid at all costs. Well, surprise, surprise. It's the *single* guys you have to watch out for.

Luckily, both types are easy to spot. Married men are the ones without wedding rings. Single guys wear them—to fend off commitment.

You think I'm kidding, but I'm not. Any single man worth his salt will guard his bachelor status as vigilantly (some might say as incomprehensibly) as a eunuch protecting a harem. Because in both cases, the question has to arise: what for?

Seriously, exactly what higher destiny are these bachelor boys saving themselves to fulfil? Nobody knows. The ones under forty live in disgusting tacky highrise apartments with green plastic balconies, parquet floors so warped that fog collects in low-lying areas, and a hamperful of dirty socks whose smell would stop a quartz watch. These slum-like conditions are what they fondly refer to as their "independent lifestyle".

Meanwhile, the ones over forty make a very big deal about still wanting to meet the right girl, settle down and so forth, before it's too late. Uh-huh. So why is it they make it a policy never to date anyone whose age or I.Q. is over sixteen? Need to be within earshot of the sound of a Masarati engine in order to become sexually aroused? Can't talk for more than five minutes consecutively about anything except bearer bonds, the right way to make a gin gimlet, and tennis racquets?

Single men, as you can see, are the secret of married men's charms. At least we don't expect anything of another woman's husband, and we can also rely on her to handle all the grubby details, like nagging him, cutting his corns, and suffering through the fourth recounting of how he landed the Brenner contract right under the nose of the competition.

Meanwhile the fun stuff is left for us Other Women – the intimate little dinners, guaranteed romantic because of the necessity of choosing dark restaurants; the stolen weekends in New York (or do we only think of them as stolen because that was the trip our hotel room got burgled?). Not to mention the particularly exhilarating thrill of falling asleep beside a man who definitely promises to be gone by the time we wake up, taking his morning breath and day's growth of beard with him.

Which, however, sister mine, is not to suggest there is no down side to the whole business of leasing other women's spouses (spice?) on a short-term basis. And I'm not talking about all that old-fashioned tear-jerking *Back Street* stuff, about Other Women spending statutory holidays alone and having to hang up when his wife answers and all that.

No. What I'm talking about is the troubles that begin the very first time you even bring a married guy back to your place. For one thing, you can tell immediately it's been a long time since he's been out on the loose. He thinks everything in your place is so *groovy* (a word he last had occasion to use back in college). "Hey, wicker! Wow!" he exclaims. Or – "Candles! Far out!" And he can't get over the fact there are no kids anywhere. He keeps checking the door frames for Jolly Jumper hooks.

Of course, before he leaves for the long drive back home to the suburbs, he gives you this little speech about how lucky you are to be free. Free. Meanwhile, you could lease Alberta for what your apartment costs, and the wild downtown social life he imagines you lead largely consists of the certifiable loony from across the hall shouting obscenities through your mail slot, right?

But why should you be the one to shatter his illusions? So you don't say a word – you just nod and smile and let him head back to the jumbo split-level with the basketball hoop over the garage door, and the little woman who knows seventy-four ways to serve meat loaf, most of them edible.

Because if this nice married guy knew how things *really* are out in the single world, he'd hang himself from the Jolly Jumper.

Which is not to say that's what *you* should consider doing. Far from it. There are many marvellous things about being a girl on her own in the city, and if you just give me a minute, I know I'll come up with one. While I'm thinking about it, why don't you drop me a line, just to let me know how you're getting on and whatever, and to reassure me that you don't actively resent this barrage of sisterly advice?

As I've told you, time and again, you're a free agent, and how you choose to live your life is strictly your own concern. Just so long as you keep me posted on the gory details, right?

Only kidding, doll. Write soon.

>   Fondly,
>   Laurie

P.S. As long as you're staying at Peggy's, here's a handy pointer about the mouth-breathing. If you wake up and hear her gasping away in the other room like the soundtrack of *Seahunt*, just tiptoe into the doorway of her room and whisper, "Peggy, Richard Gere's on his way over. Do you want him to know you sleep with your mouth open?" Works like a charm every time. Remember you heard it first from

>   Your sister,
>   L.

                                        October 29
Dear Sis:
  God, I laughed myself silly when I got your letter last week.
Especially the part about Peggy's Liberty's of London scarf and
the garbage disposal. I'm just surprised she didn't elect to go
down with it, like a ship's captain or whatever.
  Anyway, your letter was so exactly like *you* that I had this
irresistible impulse to call you up for a chat, until I remembered
there's no phone here at the ashram – which makes taking the
sweater orders damned difficult, among other things.
  Donny's idea. He believes that a person's internal energy is
leached away by electrical appliances, and whereas I'm not a
hundred per cent convinced that a telephone really qualifies as
such, I have to admit a lot of my internal energy has been sapped
over the years by those thousands of marathon hours I've spent
yammering away on the blower.
  Besides which, as I keep telling myself, I'm out here to get away
from modern life, so I should be willing to put up with the minor
inconveniences. Not that it's any picnic, believe you me, stumbling out to the bog of a nippy evening, falling into badger holes
because the candle I'm carrying keeps going out. Donny won't let
us use flashlights, because apparently dry-cell batteries also sap
your internal energies. Not as much, I would have thought, as
tripping over badger holes.
  Also, it's disappointing how really poorly my curling iron performs without an electrical outlet to plug into, although I'm
certainly better off than the fellow whose hearing-aid Donny
confiscated. In fact, the only electrically charged piece of equipment Donny permits here is the sweater-shop cash register, which,
for some reason, must have a completely opposite effect on
internal energies, because every time it rings, Donny smiles.
  All of which by way of explaining why I didn't phone, and why
getting a letter from you was such a big deal. Although there was
really no need to inform me that Peggy's bird isn't actually a
penguin. I'm perfectly aware of that. In fact, my suspicions are it
isn't even a bird, although you mustn't under any circumstances
let Peggy know I said that. She adores that goddamn thing, even if
it does look like something the special effects department for
Alien scrapped because it was too scary.

My heart goes out to you being ambushed by a dinner invitation from Keith and Lily. No, I'm afraid there probably *isn't* any way out of it, not unless you're prepared to change your name, go underground with the Weathermen, and, as an added precaution, alter your fingerprints with carbolic acid.

All the years I was in the city, I never did manage to successfully avoid one of Keith and Lily's dinner summonses – or, for that matter, the well-intended invitations of any of the depressingly large number of couples I know. And no matter how promisingly the evening started out, I always came home vowing angrily to myself that some day I was going to make millions by writing a book that would instruct couples on how to behave around single people.

My idea for the title is *Things I Promise Never To Do If I Ever Become Part of a Couple*. (Catchy, eh? Manages to walk that thin line between steely-eyed determination and pushy didacticism, with the added bonus touch of optimism in the hint that singledom is not forever.) And right there smack dab on the top of page one will appear the First Commandment every couple should obey if they expect to associate with single people on an ongoing basis: Thou Shalt Not Flaunt Thy Personal Happiness in Front of the Guest.

Lily and Keith, as I'm afraid you're about to find out, are big offenders in this category. Actually, my own personal suspicion is that, in reality, they hate each other's guts and fight like bottled scorpions as soon as the company walks out the door. But just bring on an audience and – bingo, it's showtime.

I mean, I can't count the number of times I went over there for dinner, only to sit stalwartly forking up my salad and pretending not to notice as Lily and Keith played footsies under the table. Or sat stolidly staring at the TV, with them on the couch beside me, giggling and nudging each other like erotic toddlers, or else groaning suggestively as they began to fondle each other in a way that seemed, out of the corner of my eye, strangely experimental for a couple who've been married six years.

Better even than that was going out some place with them, and plodding all alone in their wake as they skipped along the sidewalk ahead of me, hand-in-hand like Hansel and Gretel.

Still, for all their faults, I have to put Lily and Keith miles ahead of another couple I know called the Shipleys, to whom I am seriously considering dedicating the section of my book entitled "For Pity's Sake, No Pity", since – as you will quickly discover if you happen to meet these people and they decide to make a charitable project out of you as they did out of me – this is the type of couple who regards singledom as a tragic wasting illness.

Every time I saw the Shipleys (which was, believe me, less and less often as the years went by), they would study me with moist brown eyes like wet Bridge Mix and say, "Oh Laurie, dear, how *are* you? Getting along?" You know what I mean. As though it was a leg I was lacking instead of a date.

"I don't know how you do it," Mary Shipley would say to me admiringly, if I'd been between boyfriends for more than a week. "So wonderfully brave. Coming home alone, day after day, week after week, month after month. I don't know what I would have done if I'd ever been without a man in my life for even one instant, which, thank God, I never have been." At this point, of course, she leans over to kiss Roger, her husband. "Thank you, Roger. Thank you, darling, for being here."

Terrific. Don't mind me, folks. I'll just slip quietly out and drink some Sani-Flush.

Worst of all, of course, are those meddlesome do-gooder types who apparently think the reason you don't have a man to bring over to their place for dinner is because you don't know anybody dull and ineffectual enough to consider asking. So they step in to rectify the situation by asking someone for you. His name is Dwayne; he is a sales representative for a plastic wading pools concern. His hobbies are ice-fishing and browsing through the Consumers Distributing catalogue. Dwayne begins every sentence with "Let me put it this way."

To the kind of couple who introduces the Dwaynes into our lives, and then offers us no handy hints on how to get rid of them, I will address the chapter of my book called "Leave Matchmaking to the E. B. Eddy Company", but I doubt that even that will be sufficient to deter them.

Poor little sis, an innocent lamb making her way onto the Ark unaccompanied; I can only hope that a kissy-face evening with Lil and Keith doesn't bum you out completely.

By the way and for what it's worth, I very much second your

decision to move out of Peggy's as soon as you locate an apartment of your own. God love her, she's a peach of a woman and generosity itself, but I always felt that I made a mistake in sharing a place with someone who had so many tiny peculiarities. Tell me, does she still suck her thumb while she watches television?

Love from
Big Sister Laurie

December 11

Sister mine:

Christmas coming up, and the entire countryside is blanketed in a mantle of white. No snow yet. It's just the aftermath of that explosion at the nearby cornstarch factory you may have seen on the news.

Not much seasonal festivity of any kind around here, I'm afraid. Suddenly and inexplicably, we aren't doing a sideline in discount sweaters any more, and Donny is trying to persuade us that we can maintain our economic independence by selling local cheese instead.

Maybe we could, if it really *were* local cheese. As it is, we work from sun-up to midnight peeling the Kraft labels off the big rounds of Gouda and Cheddar that arrive in camouflage-painted trucks from the city, and replace them with "Made at the Karma Konsciousness Meditation Centre" stickers.

Myself, I can't help feeling it's a shade dishonest, to which Donny replies: "What dishonest? You think a bunch of meditation freaks could make a cheese as good as Kraft?"

While I can't really argue with him on that, I do try to point out that, if I had wanted to indulge in insincere, underhanded, and misleading business practices, I never would have given up my job in telephone sales. To which Donny replies, "Yeah, but this way you beat the morning rush-hour." There's something to that, I suppose.

But that's enough about me. After all, it seems as if you're the one with all the exciting news. First let me say how absolutely bowled over I was to read in your letter that a dinner party thrown by Keith and Lily could actually serve as the launch-pad for a romance between you and anything even faintly humanoid.

And this man – Greg, is it? – certainly sounds humanoid. Much more than humanoid. Downright angeloid is what he sounds. Of all the dumb luck, and here I am, so damned deserving and the older of us two. All those years of gritting my teeth through endless Keith-and-Lily dinners, and not once did I ever come home with anything more exciting than salmonella.

Well, well. I can't wait to meet Greg, and hopefully I will soon, provided the Kraft Hands don't swoop down and pay a midnight visit to our little operation here, spreading retributive justice along with the Miracle Whip.

You ask me how soon a person is supposed to know whether a casual affair has potential to be a long-term relationship. I suggest you not rush into anything with Greg. After all, you've still got almost three weeks in which to qualify for the substantial tax benefit that will result by marrying him before the New Year.

Seriously, though, my rules of thumb in assessing a new beau as likely husband-and-father material were always pretty basic and straightforward: (1) Does he speak any known language? If not, how quickly could he be taught to communicate with spelling blocks? (2) How considerate is he? I'm not asking for miracles in this department. Just so long as he remembers to clear the lipstick-stained cigarette butts out of the ashtray after he borrows my car to drive his father to church. (3) Is he the sensitive type? I would say so, provided that he doesn't open phone conversations with "Hi, how's it hangin'?" Provided that he doesn't think that Kurosawa is a type of dirt bike. Provided that he understands that pointing out younger, skinnier, taller, blonder, and bustier women to me on the street is not a public service. (4) Could he be termed a lively companion? That depends. Does a mirror fog up when held near his nose or mouth? Does he actually own a pair of shoes? (Whether he ever has occasion to put them on is immaterial.) Has his name cropped up recently in the death notices?

Perhaps, between the lines, you can discern the subtle suggestion that you *not blow this thing*. The good ones are too goddamn rare to jeopardize your new relationship by making extravagant demands on him – such as insisting that he bathe.

Above all, do not, under any circumstances, allow yourself to be suckered into a fight with him. Guys are always looking to break off with you over some triviality – usually the day before the

Superbowl, so they can assure themselves of the opportunity to watch the game in peace.

I remember one guy I used to go out with – Clifford, his name was – who used to break up with me regularly, just before Christmas, Valentine's Day, and my birthday, simply to save himself the expense of buying me a present. Then, a day or two after the event, he'd be on the phone, insisting it was all a misunderstanding.

Clifford could come up with the most amazing pretexts for arguments, too. One day, when I told him the sky was blue, he accused me of being "narrow-minded". Another time, he yelled at me for an hour for throwing out his favorite tie. It was a twist-tie from a garbage bag. How was I to know?

Not that I haven't contributed to the world's supply of Inane Reasons to Pick a Fight, mind you. I lost a fabulous guy named Jim Purvis just because I felt he wasn't demonstrative enough. True, for the first six months we went out together, he called me Miss Chesterfield. Then, the night he asked me to sleep with him, he insisted we flip a coin to see who got the upper bunk. And, as it turned out, his idea of a "dirty weekend" was cleaning out the cellar. Still, I didn't have to be so hard on him. Looking back on it, there was a certain kind of Old World charm in a man who would shake hands after sex.

Well, that's enough advice to the lovelorn for one letter, don't you think? I'm so glad you found yourself that apartment. It sounds absolutely perfect, and after more than three months of multiple co-habitation, I envy you the misanthropic joys of living alone. Much luck with both the new home and the new fellah. Hope they're both warm, well-equipped, and free of bugs.

As ever (unfortunately!)
Laurie

February 18

Petite Soeur:

Oh boy, what can I say? It seems no sooner have I adjusted to the notion of my itsy-bitsy baby sister wif a gweat big boyfwiend all her own than you write to announce you and Greg are getting married!

Now, not to lecture you in a moralistic fashion, but in my day, doncha know, we didn't do things that way. No siree. I mean, we were products of the sixties, right? And what we came to question in the sixties was why two people should leap into getting married, making an artificial commitment to society, at the same time putting themselves into a bind of unrealistic ideals, hopeless expectations, and inevitable disappointments? Instead, what we elected to do was to leap into living together, making a determined effort to spit in the eye of everything our parents stood for, at the same time putting ourselves into a bind of half-baked promises, limited expectations, and inevitable disappointments.

I trust you see my point. Married or not, you're going to have to go through the whole adjustment thing of living with a man – which, like eating raw oysters, you really ought to do at least once, if only so that you can tell your grandchildren that you can't understand what all the fuss is about anything so totally unappetizing, completely unsatisfying, and remarkably difficult to swallow.

As you know, I myself have more than a little first-hand experience in this department, having lived with a number of gentlemen in my time, some of them for extended periods as long as three weeks. So I thought perhaps you might benefit from some of the things I have learned from this particularly harrowing brand of so-called "hands-on" experience.

1) Under no circumstances must you ever pay the slightest attention to him when he says that he wants to be woken up early on Saturday morning. The simple truth of the matter is that he doesn't, whether it's to clear out the study, get an early start to the cottage, or finish up the work he brought home from the office. At eight o'clock on a Saturday morning – irrespective of what he said at 11:57 the previous evening – there can be only one possible reason that he's being shaken awake. And that is because you are a neurotic, overbearing, and possibly sadistic human being who simply can't stand the sight of a man asleep with a smile on his face.

2) Expect him to be moody. Contrary to the rumors spread by men, we're not the ones given to fits of despondency, irritability, and black despair. Nor should you expect to know what it is that

might have set him off. A badly worded blurb on the back of the cereal box; an item in the paper crediting a detested college rival with the cure for cancer; a humiliating failure in attempting to jump the guardrail in the parking lot. Whatever the root cause, the results will be pretty much the same. Sudden outbursts of criticism about the way you whistle "We Kiss in a Shadow" as you measure out the coffee. Gloomy allusions to the fact that it's time he thought about making a will. Snappish demands that you call up the super and give him hell for sneakily raising the height of the parking-lot guardrail without telling anyone.

3) Bear in mind that when you insult his movie heroes, you insult him. While on the surface a balding thirty-eight-year-old cost accountant with Boston lenses and a trick knee may appear to have absolutely nothing in common with Charles Bronson, underneath he thinks of Chuck as his soul-brother. So, unless you look forward to hearing retaliatory cracks about *The Way We Were*, leave *Death Wish* strictly alone.

4) Don't hide things in places where he can't find them. Cutlery placed in a kitchen drawer or a hammer secreted in a toolbox are lost forever. And while you're at it, stop concealing his shoes on the floor of the closet, stashing the evening paper in the magazine stand, squirrelling his Cross pen away in the breast pocket of his suit-jacket, and sneaking the ice-cube trays into the freezer. There's only so much gaslighting a man can take.

5) Do whatever is within your limited powers to ensure that the sexual component in your relationship remains of a high order. Because, Lord knows, *he* isn't going to take any responsibility for keeping them colored lights going. Expressions that you never expected to hear from the lips of a college graduate – such as, "What say we hit the old sackeroo?" – will gradually begin to replace the more appetizing invitations to dalliance he used to issue in the good old days before you lived together. A man for whom sleeping nude was previously almost an article of faith will suddenly acquire pyjamas and dressing-gowns that appear to be straight out of the wardrobe closet of Fred MacMurray. Seductive creams, balms, and unguents that you fetch home from the local sex shop to revitalize your relationship will be used to soothe mosquito bites. Worst of all, when you're out at the movies together, you will notice him slipping out for popcorn during the love scenes, and hurrying back just in time for the car chase.

If, after reading all of the above, you still think you're prepared to throw caution to the winds and leap into this relationship, more power to you.

And of course I'll be delighted to accept the role of Maid of Honor at the wedding – although at this point in my sprawling career, the more accurate job description might be Made Without Honor.

But listen, if I'm going to don those pale-mauve peau-de-soie shoes for you, not to mention shelling out something in the neighborhood of three bills for a bell-skirted acetate number that will, after the ceremony, never serve any practical purpose in my wardrobe again (unless I get invited to a costume party where everyone is requested to come as Sandra Dee), then there's something you really ought to do for me in return: give me first dibs on that dishy-sounding little apartment of yours.

This is not a joke. I've made my mind up to leave the ashram, and if, as you indicate, you plan to be moving into Greg's place after the honeymoon, then I'd love to snap up your little joint.

Yeah, yeah, I know. I was the one who was through with the urban rat race, and wild horses weren't going to drag me back into the endless round of pest control, snagged pantyhose, eating Chinese on Friday night with the girls, unreturned phone calls, patronizing gynaecologists, dying benjaminas, strap-hangers with Walkmen, eating Italian on Saturday night with the girls, sexual innuendoes from the young hood in the mail room, Christmas shopping at noon hour, eating Middle Eastern on Sunday night with the girls, sexual innuendoes from the octogenarian running the elevator, being passed over for promotion, and sexual innuendoes from the menopausal lech up at Head Office – all the things that are, in point of sad fact, actually the bright spots of the life of a single woman in the city.

But the truth of the matter is, ever since we scrapped the cheese operation here at the ashram, and opened up the bingo parlor instead, things have become so hectic that I feel that I need to go back to town, if only to catch up on my sleep.

Not only that, I become more and more convinced that the faintly illicit nature of many of Donny's business enterprises is simply not compatible with the principles of meditation, inner integrity, and spiritual enlightenment that Karma Konsciousness is supposed to stand for.

I don't know if I told you, but it turns out that the discontinuation of the discount sweater outlet had some vague connection with a Mafia purge in Palermo. About the cheese scam, you will remember, I was qualmy right from the outset.

Unfortunately, the enterprises that have replaced them – not only the bingo, but also sales of pirated rock videos, a lottery fraud, and the dog-track – all have a slightly unsavory quality to them that I can't quite put my finger on, except that a suspicious number of new arrivals at the commune bear more than a passing resemblance to Richard Widmark.

Aw well, live and learn, eh?

Of course, whenever I tell Donny I'm leaving, his face turns approximately the same shade as those peau-de-soie shoes you're ordering for your bridal party, and he begins muttering something about how if I desert the ashram, I can expect to wind up "sleeping with the fishes".

Hey, I tell him, no problem. Considering that I currently sleep with cooties the size of fox terriers, the fishes will make a nice change, no?

Congratulations, sugar-bun, take care and let me know toot sweet about the suite, y'heah? I expect to be back in the city in time for spring when, in the park, the dog turds will just be beginning to push their tentative way through the snow, and when, from a balcony ledge, a hunk of dirty slush with my name on it will be poised and ready to fall.

It's been a pleasure corresponding with you.

Your spiritually enlightened sister,
Laurie

the
answering
machine

I don't remember exactly when it was that I first became interested in telephone-answering-machine tapes, and the evidence they might provide of how life was lived back in the faraway days of the late twentieth century.

Of course, I'd already done a considerable amount of research on twentieth-century artifacts. My Ph.D. thesis, entitled *Office Desk Ornaments as Mirrors of the Struggle for Individuation in a Depersonalized Work Milieu*, contains a chapter on coffee-cup slogans ("'It's Not My Job': A Stirring Plea for Understanding") that, I have been told, is now regarded as a definitive examination of the subject.

Later, however, I began to perceive the limitations of zodiac mugs, Snoopy statuettes, and Cathy Guisewite pencil caddies as means through which to approach the quotidian life of the period. Yet, what other research material was there at my disposal? None, I thought.

As we know, by the eighth decade of the twentieth century, letter-writing and diary-keeping had all but disappeared, thus depriving future anthropologists and sociologists of many incidentally valuable insights into the society of the time. Indeed, all important interpersonal communication was, by the year 1980, carried on over lunch.

Therefore, for a long time – too long – I discounted the possibility that there existed any permanent record of how twentieth-century man communicated, and what he communicated about.

Until, that is, I stumbled, by happy accident, upon the answering machine. To my embarrassment, I must confide that I did not immediately recognize the machine for the invaluable data repository that it is. In fact, for months I labored under the illusion that the device was some primitive form of food processor, nearly destroying its delicate mechanism in my attempts to see what it could do in the direction of puréeing carrots, bananas, and other vegetable matter.

When it turned out that the answering machine fared poorly with everything except parboiled tomatoes, I gradually began to suspect my error. Only then began the long process of re-identifying the machine correctly. I tell you, that moment when I pushed the Start button and played the first of its tapes – as blobs of inadequately diced tomato came splattering out of the motor – was an exciting moment indeed for science.

The earliest research that I completed in the answering-machine field was on what is known, in technical parlance, as the *announce tape* – that is, the tape upon which the owner of the machine records his or her message bidding callers to leave their messages in return. Deceptively simple in purpose, the announce tape offers almost infinite variations in terms of what it can tell the scientist about the person who recorded it and, by extrapolation, a great deal about the social context in which that person existed.

By way of example, let me offer you selected excerpts from my lengthy research paper entitled *The Cottswangle Tapes: A Beeps Diary of Their Time* in which the announce tapes of a young twentieth-century freelance writer named David Cottswangle are examined over a ten-year period, as a means of illuminating the changes and developments that occurred socially and economically, not only in the life of the young man Cottswangle, but also in the late-twentieth-century milieu in which he lived.

Cottswangle's initial foray into the crafting of an announce tape runs as follows: "Uh . . . hi, this is David. . . . I'm not here right now, okay? But, like, you can leave a message. Um . . . after the beep."

Well. The guilelessness, the blundering ingenuousness of a technologically unsophisticated age speaks for itself, I think. Here is a young inarticulate man, living on his own for the first time, poised on the brink of discovering the riches that a prosperous but somehow oddly naive society can offer him.

The time, you must remember, is the mid-1970s. The economic

climate is salubrious, fertile, pulsing with expectation. . . . Is it any wonder that writer David Cottswangle experiences deep inchoate emotions that can only find their expression in straightforward unadorned honesty? "I'm not here right now, okay?" As though the speaker senses somehow with the confidence of youth and hope that it *will* be okay, if that's the way he wants it.

Two years later, his announce tape underscores even more clearly the quality of confident ease that was the hallmark both of the times and of men like Cottswangle. "Hi, it's Dave. As the late great Dotty Parker was wont to say, I'm afraid I'm too fucking busy – or vice versa – to come to the phone right now, but. . ."

It's significant to note that during this period the country (Canada) is surging with energetic activity in all fields of artistic endeavor, while David Cottswangle, like the country he lives in, enjoys an unimpeded sense of creative outpouring. Dave now writes film scripts for the burgeoning Canadian movie industry, and one of his screenplays, *Bloody Entrails*, is under consideration by a major (i.e. American) producer. The identification with Dorothy Parker is, therefore, neither entirely unconscious, nor without relevance.

Alas, what a different world it is for Cottswangle when we tune in on an announce tape from several years later, in the recession-battered year of 1982. "You have reached the residence of David J. Cottswangle," the tape intones, without inflection or humor. "Although no one is available right now to take your call, if you'd be good enough to leave your name and number at the sound of the beep, then. . ."

Almost by instinct, we can divine what vicissitudes the intervening years have brought. Economic hardship, the virtual collapse in both funding and credibility of the film industry in Canada. . . .

For David personally, the end of the boom years has meant seeing *Bloody Entrails* go into turnaround with three different studios, a failure to get his next effort, *Axe Murder Weekend*, optioned by anyone, even the CBC, as well as a writing block the size of Venezuela. Is it any wonder that his announce tape projects a tone of clipped impersonality, masking financial anxiety and anticipation of certain rejection?

With what overwhelming relief, then, do we divine from auditing a yet later announce tape that David's fortunes have taken, in the mid-1980s, a definite turn for the better. The off-again-on-again world of the cinema is a thing of the past; instead, David has done the sensible thing, and taken a job at an advertising agency.

"Hi there," declares his answering machine, with some of the breezy insouciance of old, "Dave Cottswangle speaking. What's *your* story? No, seriously, I'm interested. At the sound of the beep, kindly leave your. . ."

Pretty glib stuff, perhaps. But it's nice to hear, isn't it, that Dave's feeling better, and to know that the economy of the time has likewise taken a sharp upward turn?

A new job, better prospects, a rosier future all round. In addition, another positive element has become a part of Cottswangle's life, and will soon reflect itself in his announce tapes. David has met a girl.

Whence, you ask, comes such certain knowledge of the intimate workings of the subject's private life? Not solely from the announce tape, surely, which provides only the most general information about the state of David Cottswangle's mental and fiscal well-being.

No, not solely from the announce tape. You're quite correct. There is, in fact, another component of the answering machine's inventory of rich and startling personal information – *the message tape*.

As the name suggests, the message tape is where were recorded the messages left by those long-ago telephone callers who reached the machine instead of the person they had dialled.

Examination of early message tapes from the Cottswangle machine reveals little of real interest to the social anthropologist. There are the predictable calls from friends ("Hi, Dave. Jerry. Hey, what's the machine doing on this hour of the morning? You get lucky last night, or what?"), as well as more subtextually weighty communiqués from members of the immediate family.

For instance, a typical message from David's mother runs as follows: "Hello, David, you won't remember me probably, but I'm the one who gave up a promising concert career in order to be there after school every day when you got home. Or perhaps you might better recall me as the person you mailed your laundry to from college? Don't bother returning my call. I really just wanted to hear how your voice sounds since it changed."

It's only when serious romance enters Cottswangle's life, in the form of one Elly Larson, that the message tapes become richly indicative of the most complex social patterns of the late twentieth century.

Elly's debut on David's machine is hardly an auspicious one, offering as it does little hint of the important role she will come to play in his life. "Oh, hello. . . . Uh, you don't know me, but my name is Elly and what I'm calling about is, you put this ad in the *Ward Six Herald* for a typist to work on a novel manuscript? Anyway, I'm a typist and – Oh look, I'm not too good with these machines. I'll call back when you're home, okay?"

The only fact of real interest contained in the foregoing is Elly's reference to a novel that David has evidently written. Apparently he did not regard his ad agency job as an adequate creative replacement for his abandoned film career, and from that we may legitimately, I think, adduce the probable existence of a multitude of novel manuscripts in the locked desk drawers of a large number of advertising copywriters of the period.

In spite of Elly's obvious discomfiture at dealing with an answering machine, she must have eventually honored her promise to call back, because the next thing we know, the manuscript is typed, and Elly is leaving a message to that effect. Note how much more confidently she has come to deal with the problem of speaking on tape.

"Hi, Dave, it's Elly Larson, and I'm just letting you know you can pick up the last section of the book any time, okay? I – well, this sounds kind of silly, but I'm sorry to be finished in a way, if you want the truth. I think it's a really good book. No kidding. It's the most fun I ever had typing anything . . . ever. Well, 'bye. . . . "

To Dave, there was evidently nothing at all silly in what Elly had said, and the end of their business relationship by no means spelled the end of their ongoing association. A sampling of more message tapes authored by Elly over the next few weeks tells the continuing tale:

"Hi, Dave. It's Elly Larson. My sister Sherry told me you called? I hope it isn't about typing – I mean – oh nuts, what I mean is, I – uh – have a pretty full plate of work right now and . . . Oh well. Just call me, I guess. 'Bye."

"Hi, Dave. Elly. All I called to say is . . . I really enjoyed last night. Thanks for dinner and . . . it was fun talking. 'Bye."

"Dave, Elly. Look, I'm really sorry I couldn't get together last night, but I gather from Sherry she managed to entertain you okay, and knowing Sherry, you probably didn't miss me at *all*. Ha ha, only kidding. Call me, okay?"

"Hi, sweetheart, it's me. Look, did I leave my chiffon scarf over there? I've looked everywhere. Hey. . . it was a beautiful evening. Really."

"Oh, Dave, honey, I just got your message from Sherry about the book and I'm really sorry. Those publishers must be jerks, that's all, and anyway, I love you, whether you're published or not, okay?"

"Dave, it's me and, grrr, you'll never guess what: the key you had made for me doesn't fit your door. Half my wardrobe's locked up in your apartment and I have a job interview this aft. Help!"

"Look, sweetheart, I'm calling to apologize for being so bitchy before, okay? Of course I'll spend the weekend at your place again. . . . It's just that I get so fed up schlepping my clothes back and forth, and of course my place is always out of the question because of Sherry. . . . Oh hell. Anyway, pick me up at the office, okay? And – oh, I'm sorry the book came back again. Honest."

An astute observer of human nature will by now have already guessed the next logical development in the saga of David and Elly. However, for the sake of those who are somewhat slower on the uptake, here is a transcript of the next announce tape that was recorded on Dave's machine:

"Hi, this is Dave and Elly. Well, actually, it's me, Dave, but if you have a message for either me or Elly, or both of us, or – Oh, what the heck. Just leave your name and number after the beep, all right? Ciao."

And then, later, once both David and Elly have obviously become more accustomed to their new domestic situation as a fact of life not likely to disappear in the blinking of an eye:

"Hi, Elly and I aren't able to come to the phone right now, but leave a message after the beep, and just as soon as we finish having another hilariously warm-hearted time making pasta together, we'll. . . "

But, alas, the course of true love never did run smooth, no more in that bygone era of the 1980s than in our own day. Despite the sense of harmony implied by that last tape, all too soon problems on many fronts began to arise, as a cursory examination of several of their subsequent message tapes readily confirms.

First, there were the evident efforts at readjustment both families had to make. "David? It's your mother. At least, I think it's your mother, unless by some lucky chance I've got the wrong number. I certainly hope so. I certainly hope no son of mine would invite stray females into his home to cohabitate with him, and then advertise the fact to the entire world by putting it on his answering machine. David, for heaven's sake. What if your boss should call you at home? What's he going to think?"

"Elly, it's Sherry, and you walked off with my blue angora sweater. Also, will you please tell all your friends you've moved in at Dave's? I'm sick of answering your calls, and they always phone when I'm in the shower."

In addition, there were the inevitable ego-battering pressures of modern life that both David and Elly had to cope with.

"This is a message for David Cottswangle from Melissa Faraday at Aladdin Press. I'm afraid I haven't had a chance to take a look at the revised version of your novel yet, so could we put off lunch again, until next week?"

"Elly, it's Frank Carson from work. Look, I had no idea Sherry Larson was your sister. I mean, she's so absolutely gorgeous and everything that – Uh, er, what I mean is, El, could I possibly have her number? I'd really like to give her a call."

But where the real domestic melodrama begins to unfold itself is in the message tapes of David and Elly to each other, many of which contain not only the clues to the gradual disintegration of their relationship, but also valuable insights into the psychosexual dynamic operative in male-female interactions of the time.

"El? I – look, I won't be in till late. I got the bad news from Aladdin Press today about the book and . . . well, I think I'll head out to the bar with some of the guys after work and try to forget I ever thought about being a writer. . . . "

"David, for God's sake, I can't believe you still aren't home. This is the third night this week, and how long can I stay in this bar with Frank Carson listening to him cry into his beer because Sherry apparently dumped him for some other guy that even *I* haven't heard her mention anything about?"

"Dave, it's me, and I'm just checking in to say don't expect dinner on the table when you get home, because I have an appointment to see this Dr. Proctor one of the girls at work

recommended. I know what you think about therapy and everything, but I really have to do something. . . . "

"Elly, Sherry called up with an extra ticket to the Stones, and if
it's okay with you, I'm gonna go with her. Sorry, but if you didn't
spend all your time on that head-candler's couch, you wouldn't
miss out."

"Dave, goddamn it all, this is the last straw! I just came out of Dr.
Proctor's office, where I'd spent the entire *hour* telling him I knew
my suspicions about you and Sherry are groundless, and what do I
see? You and Sherry strolling arm in arm out of Eaton's! David –
my own sister! How long has this been going on?"

And then, at last, inevitably, another announce tape crops up on
the machine, to relate the final chapter with a sort of laconic
eloquence that is almost as poignantly pathetic today as it must
have been the day it was recorded.

"Hi, this is Dave Cottswangle. I'm not here right now, but I'll be
back soon, so leave your message after the beep. If you're calling
for Elly Larson, she can now be reached at 586-9292."

But what of Elly, you may ask? Did she go on to acquire her own
answering machine, upon which to inscribe the record of the
species of new and promising social life we must all by now feel she
so richly deserved?

Unfortunately not. At least, not as far as I know. However,
shortly after I finished my detailed examination of the Cottswangle Tapes, another set of answering-machine tapes came into my
possession. You can imagine my surprise and elation when these
tapes turned out to be from the files of Dr. Hector Proctor, Elly
Larson's therapist.

Since it is not my purpose here to provide an exhaustive analysis
of any but the Cottswangle Tapes, let me simply – by way of
furnishing a sort of coda to the entire David-and-Elly saga –
present the salient portions of the Proctor transcripts, as they
apply to the next chapter in the continuing story of the deeply
troubled Miss Larson.

"This is Dr. Hector Proctor. I'm not in the office right now, but
it's important that you not take this as a sign of rejection. At the
sound of the tone, leave your name and number, and the nature of
your neurosis, and I'll get back to you, just as soon as the tennis
season is over."

"Dr. Proctor? This is Elly Larson – Wednesdays at ten? You said I should let you know if I had any more dreams about Sherry. You remember Sherry, my amoral but stunningly beautiful sister? The one who's stolen my last six boyfriends away?

"Well, I had this nightmare that I was shipwrecked on an island in the South Pacific with Sherry. Alone. For nine years. Nine years, and Sherry's tennis dress is still spanking white. And she's learned to make her own cream rinse out of palm fronds. I meanwhile have been forced to stitch a dress together out of some oars.

"And for nine years I've had to listen to Sherry tell and retell the plot of *Rome Adventure*, starring Troy Donahue. In this dream, Doctor, Sherry's adapted to island life, and I haven't. She's made friends of the animals who are tamable, and flattering coats out of the animals who aren't.

"She's found a way to get *Glamour* magazine delivered to the island, and she's accessorized her primitive wardrobe four hundred and fifty ways. I, meanwhile, am still wondering what kind of purse to wear with the oars.

"And just at this point in the dream, Doctor, this great-looking guy – he looks kind of like you – washes up on our beach, wearing nothing but a pair of Speedo trunks and some Bain de Soleil. And when he revives, and opens his eyes, the first things he sees are me and Sherry. Sherry with a nine-year suntan, and me with a bad heat rash.

"But it's *me* he beckons to him, Doctor, and I get down beside him very close, and he whispers, 'Baby, take off them oars.' And when I take them off – quick as a flash, he produces an outrigger from behind some shrubs, and whisks Sherry into it, and they both row off into the South Pacific, leaving me there, naked, with a bad heat rash! Dr. Proctor, please call me back and tell me what this dream means!"

"Hello, this is Dr. Hector Proctor. I'm not in the office at the moment. However, if this is Elly Larson calling, I have a special message for you, Elly.

"Take no notice of your nightmares. They are paranoic distortions that have nothing to do with reality. Should you have further questions, write to me in care of your sister Sherry, somewhere in the South Pacific. Goodbye."

The Sun Also Sets

Excuse me. Sir? Excuse me? Hi. I wonder if I can speak to you for a moment, about a subject that's very close to my heart – the plight of the suntanner.

No, don't walk away. Please. Oh, I know you're tired of people like me – people you think of as earnest nature-nuts, each of us pleading the cause of some endangered species or other. I can imagine you've pretty well had it up to here with the peregrine falcon, the wild mustang, and, yes, even the lovable humpbacked whale.

But won't you give some thought – just for one brief instant – to how much poorer a place the world will be if the noble *aestivus parbroilus* – better known to you as the summer suntanner – is allowed to just vanish without a trace.

If you're at all familiar with the natural history of this land, you'll know that once upon a time, the beaches were covered as far as the eye could see with suntanners – paging through dog-eared copies of *The Thornbirds*, picking flecks of sand from their coconut-oiled navels, or merely lying in the spread-eagled posture characteristic of their breed.

From Wreck Beach to Restigouche, from Cavendish to Cornwall, they roamed free, taking what sun they needed, then moving on, leaving little behind but a whiff of Noxzema and the occasional bathhouse key, never dreaming that their simple way of life would soon be threatened with extinction.

How did it happen to the suntanner, you ask. (My overwrought rhetoric gets them every time.) Well, sir, the answer to what became of this gentle mammal, and how this wholesale destruction could have been prevented, can be summed up in a single word: superstition and greed. You're right, sir, that's actually *two* words. I tend to get carried away and forget grammatical niceties.

In any case, it's not a pretty saga; such stories seldom are. It is, rather, a story of inhumanity, evil, and blind prejudice – the kind of ingredients that make for both bitter memories and a dynamite movie sale (providing, of course, that you have a star in place and can get Spielberg to direct).

Back in the beginning, you see, back before the bad times came, when every conceivable piece of shoreline was dotted with sunbathers and it seemed that summer would never end, the clouds of ignorance and misundertanding had already begun to gather.

First came the ignorant and the bigoted, with their unsubstantiated rumors that the sun was "bad for the skin". Genteel ladies under parasols, their arms covered with gauze; pale-skinned intellectuals to whom a bronzed hide represented brainless hedonism; Calvinistic zealots sniffily disapproving of bare brown limbs.

In the face of this initial assault, the suntanners were calm, and felt no sense of foreboding. Surely, they thought in their peaceable and slightly sunstruck way, the beach was big enough to accommodate all schools of opinion. Surely the anti-suntan fanatics meant them no harm.

Well, harm *was* meant, but might never have come to pass, had not the belligerently bigoted found some unexpected allies within the world of science. These were the dermatologists – swaggering adventurers with nothing to lose and a sophisticated arsenal of weapons at their command, including statistics on the incidence of sun-related skin cancer and research on premature aging, to name but two.

Unprepared as the suntanners were for this sudden attack, and too encumbered by beach blankets and thermos jugs to make a speedy escape, they were felled in their thousands by the dermatologists' onslaught, and the beach was a noticeably barer place.

For those small, hardy herds that remained, survival ought to have been assured, except that the skin doctors were then joined in their unholy sport by other branches of the scientific community.

That's right, sir. At this point, the nutritionists arrived on the scene, determined to starve out what was left of the suntanners, by eliminating their food supply. Batter-fried chicken was the first suntanning staple to go, followed in rapid succession by bacon burgers, french fries, potato salad, carbonated beverages, instant iced tea, and cigarettes.

By the time cheese-corn was labelled as a possible carcinogen, the beach had been stripped of virtually every preferred munchie in the suntanners' diet, and the embattled sun-worshippers had totally lost heart – not to mention a few unsightly pounds.

For some time, the stragglers attempted to eke out an insubstantial existence on the only comestibles left to them by the nutritionists – bean sprouts, sushi, and seven-grain bread. But few of these unnatural substances could be consumed in sufficient quantities to make a filling meal, and none was available in those places where the suntanners preferred to forage – Seven-Eleven stores, which could be visited for browsing at night, after the hours of good tanning were over, anyway.

And so, weakened by hunger and unaccustomed good nutrition, the remaining suntanners fell easy prey to the last of the predators to arrive on the scene – you guessed it, sir. The environmentalists.

Some believe – and I am one of them – that this group was the most sinister enemy of them all, with its air of counterfeited concern and its deceptively straightforward ways.

While pretending to help the suntanners by branding certain lakes and river systems unsafe for swimming, the environmentalists actually robbed the few of these harmless creatures that were left of their native habitat. Favorite tanning spots like Lake Erie and the banks of the Niagara River were condemned, but no alternative tanning areas were provided.

And as if that were not sufficiently disastrous, the environmentalists dealt their deathblow to the suntanners by attacking the Winnebago, the Airstream trailer, and the Pontiac station wagon – indispensable to the tanners' nomadic way of life – as gas-guzzlers and polluters.

Which brings us, sir, right up to our own age, when all that is left, it seems, is for the scavengers to pick over the bones of a once-proud culture. The current new-wave vogue for pasty white skin suggestive of winter pallor makes, of course, a deliberate mockery of the Bronze Age that came before, and renders it an almost absolute certainty that those lazy, hazy, crazy days of summer will never come again.

Unless. Unless, sir, you are prepared to help. Oh yes, I can see what you're thinking. "Here comes the pitch." Well, I suppose it *is* a pitch, and I suppose you're sick and tired of being asked to dig down into your jeans for yet another bleeding-heart cause. But I can see by your face that you're a compassionate and sensitive person – this is no guff, sir – and the very fact that you've taken time to listen to what I have to say encourages me to feel that you'll stay at least to hear me out.

Thank you, sir. I appreciate that. You see, things have reached such a desperate pass that only a handful of suntanners constitute the difference between rejuvenation of the herds and the total extinction of the species. And most of the remaining breeding stock is, sadly, of such an advanced age that they still sing "Help Me, Rhonda" in the shower.

Why, it's gotten so bad, economically speaking, over at the Coppertone suntan products company that there's talk of having to shoot the little black spaniel in the ads, just to reduce the number of mouths to feed.

Of course, sir, that just can't be allowed to happen, which is why a group of us friends of the suntanner have launched the Back To The Bronze Age Fund, to save the noble sunbather, and why we are asking you to make a contribution.

Your money will be well spent, believe me, principally on the type of public awareness campaign that is the cornerstone of any conservation movement.

The first thing we decided was that we needed a campaign mascot – you know, someone to stand as a kind of physical embodiment of the quintessential qualities the suntanner represents.

Well, after a great deal of deliberation – and only some minor dissent – Frank Sinatra has been chosen, on the grounds that over the years and in spite of changing trends in public opinion, Ol' Blue Eyes (as we like to call him) has always courageously maintained his tan.

In fact, if you make a contribution today of ten dollars or more to the Back To The Bronze Age Fund, you will be given, absolutely free of charge, this beautiful long-playing album, which features some of the haunting songs of Frank Sinatra, captured by naturalists, as he croons eerily in the pre-dawn to other members of his kind on a remote shore of Lake Tahoe. Believe me, anyone who hears this stirring sound never forgets it, and if anything argues eloquently for the highly developed sensibilities of *aestivus parbroilus*, this album has got to be it.

Not interested? Fair enough. Then let me tell you about another area of activity we're involved in that needs your financial support – our educational and research work to raise consciousness about the important role suntanned people have played throughout history.

You know, of course, that Spartacus had a nice tan. But did you also realize that so did Fletcher Christian? Lawrence of Arabia was a suntanner. And Connie Stevens. And Paul Gauguin. . . . Well, the list goes on and on.

Aesthetically speaking, civilization would have been a poorer place without the contribution suntanners have made through the ages. It was people with tans who built the Great Pyramids, the Appian Way, the Statue of Liberty, and the first A & W rootbeer stand. The concert at Woodstock was a product of the suntanned – just take a look at the film if you don't believe me.

Also, we've uncovered data which proves conclusively that it was suntanners who gave us miniature golf, the double-decker ice-cream cone, and the Cookie-gram. No, really. It was.

Most important, we're in the process of compiling statistics that attest to the suntanners' superior way of life. I mean, we actually have evidence that suggests a person with a suntan gets fewer cavities, gives more to charity, and is a better dancer.

Which, of course, is not to say that we think the suntanner is nature's perfect species. Fantastic as they are – or, at least, as they were in their heyday – they always had their drawbacks, just like anybody else, right? Knuckle-cracking is a bad habit of suntanners. Wearing Lacoste shirts with the little alligator. Playing the accordion. And laughing at reruns of *Green Acres*. But then, nobody's perfect, as I say.

Anyway, for my money, the suntanners have come just about as close as you can get to perfect on this earth. By the bye – speaking of money. Any amount you can see your way clear to contribute to the Bronze Age Fund would be greatly appreciated. We're working on getting charitable tax status. . . .

Still not sure? Hey, no problem, I can understand that. And look – just in case you're under the impression that all of our activities centre around these polite little pleas for understanding on behalf of the suntanned, I really think I ought to tell you that there's a more militant aspect to our campaign as well.

I mean, you look like a pretty stand-up sort of guy to me, and it might interest you to know that there's a slightly more radical group of us within the organization, and we devote ourselves to attacking the enemies of suntanners, just as the suntanners themselves have been attacked and discredited over the years.

The methods we use, basically, are smear tactics and unfounded rumors. For example, we're spreading the word right now that snow contributes to premature aging, and that prolonged exposure to down-filled garments and ChapStick causes cancer. Ha ha. Pretty neat, eh? That'll certainly fix them, don't you think?

Oh come on, don't look at me like that. It's only fair. If the suntanners have to go, they're taking the skiers with them. I mean, why shouldn't –

Hey, where do you think you're going? You can't just leave. You haven't given me a donation yet, or received your Back To The Bronze Age button or anything. . . . Hey, sir. Hey!

(Darn it. Why do I always do that? Get so close, then blow it by going too far. Nobody likes a fanatic. I have to remember that. Nobody likes a –)Whoops.

Ma'am! Excuse me, ma'am. Excuse me? Hi. I wonder if I can speak to you for a moment, about a subject that's very. . .

The
Dirty
Thirties

Tell me if this rings a bell. Back in the sixties, when you were a college student, the rumor was that Prince Charles – then a mere eighteen or so – planned to attend university in Canada.

Instantly, your imagination raced on fast forward to meeting the prince in an economics class, chatting him up over a cup of bad coffee in the Student Union building – then marrying him, in a flurry of astonished headlines. "Heir to Throne Smitten by Commoner with B Average". "Canuck Co-Ed Majoring in Monarchy". Sigh.

So what if the prince came across as a bit of a goop, with those ears that looked as though they'd been created in anticipation of Dolby sound, and the kind of shoulders never intended to hold up coveralls? He was rich, he got to go on neat trips, and if you could only land him, you'd never have to work a day in your life.

Well, of course, Prince Charles wound up going to Australia instead – or joining the navy, or getting caught up in a protracted game of polo, or something. The point is, he never showed up in Canada, and you taught yourself to forget all about him. Right?

Right. Only Prince Charles wouldn't *let* you forget. A full fifteen years later, he decides all of a sudden to get married.

But does he call *you* up for old times' sake? Does he say, "Look here, I understand you were rather keen on me some years back. What say we make up for lost time and tie the knot?" He does not.

Instead, he scours the kingdom for a virgin (oh, come now) and marries Lady Di who, at nineteen, is almost exactly the age *you* were when you planned to marry him all those years ago! So how come *you* had to grow up and the prince didn't?

Because you're a woman, that's how come, and therefore uniquely able to understand why, in the newspaper business, the number "30" signifies The End. And while you're not particularly thrilled to be in your thirties, you've gone past the point where you can ignore the fact that it's happened.

For one thing, your mother appears to have shrunk. This is a dead giveaway. For another, your own kids' music seems far louder than what you used to play. Unless you're childless, in which case you find you keep cranking up the volume, just to drown out the ticking of the biological clock.

But one big consolation (not all *that* big, but something) is that you're not alone with your thirties-hood. Dear Lord no. Not only are you a woman (fifty-one per cent of the population right there), but you're also part of the generation known, rather inelegantly, as "the baby boom" – the post-World War Two reproductive glut that has meant, for you, a lifetime of never being alone, any place.

In kindergarten, there were never enough slides and teeter-totters to go around; in grade school, there were so many of you, some had their desks out in the hall. As for college? Let's not even talk about college. (Too many painful memories of being left at the altar by Prince Chuck.) Suffice it to say that, for a baby-boomer, getting into university made the Kremlin look like a drop-in centre.

Of course, because there are so many other women your age, you've arrived in your thirties to find that men are as scarce as the swings back in the playground.

Where on earth are they? They can't all be married. You had the good grace to either get divorced or stay single – why couldn't they? Nor can they all be gay – just the good-looking, interesting ones went that way.

Taking a leaf from Prince Charles' book (or Pierre Trudeau's, or Brian Mulroney's), you try to beat the odds by seeking out a younger mate. Besides, you've read that, sexually speaking, older women and younger men are both at their peak. Yum.

Ho-hum. To women of your tie-dye and brown-rice generation,

today's younger men seem shockingly corporate – sporting attaché cases instead of backpacks, and putting highrises on the land instead of going back to it.

Who *knows* if these guys are sexual dynamite? They never put down *The Financial Post* long enough for you to find out.

With a defeated sigh, you turn to Jane Fonda's Workout album, trying to take heart from Jane's taut example of what awaits you in your forties, while not resenting her *too* much for goading you into stretches you are in no way ready for in your thirties.

Yet you know – if Jane would just stop dinning in your ear long enough for you to think – that there really is an upside (as your Young Corporate Boyfriend would say) to this whole business of being thirty-plus.

For one thing – and this is key (as your Y.C.B. would also say) – you're finally beyond the age when you even need to *consider* a roommate. So what if your fifth-floor bachelor walk-up is so small the milk chute counts as an extra bedroom? It's all yours: your (grey) hairs in the bathroom drain, your negligence that murdered the schefflera.

And if you're living with a man, you're well past the stage where you have to draw up those boring feminist contracts to determine who changes the beds and who mows the lawn. Neither one of you does. Every six months, provided the relationship is still intact, you simply move.

Another big advantage of your recent maturity is that you're finally adult enough to stand up to your hairdresser. Don't make the mistake of underrating this achievement. The Croix de Guerre has been awarded for less.

And in clothing stores, you need not even pretend to take an interest in the New Wave look, thank God.

There. You see? It's really not all that bad, this business of being over thirty. No, really. Come on, now – stop sticking pins into that Princess Di doll and listen to me. It's not that bad. Honest.

Working It Out

I think maybe my friend Yvonne has gone too far with this "working out" business. Last week, she accidentally bent a vacuum cleaner attachment just taking it out of the cupboard. Yesterday she tore a towel in two, merely trying to wring it out. And this morning she was stopped on her way to the grocery store by a policeman who advised her that she would have to drop down to the station house to have her biceps registered as Dangerous Weapons.

I don't believe for a minute that Yvonne *planned* it that way. That first day, when she wandered into the gym in quest of a few exercises to help her with her unsightly midriff bulge, the farthest thing from her mind was the possibility that she would emerge, six months later, with upper arms as rippled and polished as braided bread, and thighs so taut you can bounce nickels off them.

So, what happened? What was the subtle psychological process that transformed my friend Yvonne from a mild-mannered housewife looking to get back into last summer's sundress into a muscle-bound Amazon for whom a day without bench-presses is like a day without sunshine?

I have resolved to find out.

Actually, I've been meaning to get myself enrolled in some sort of exercise program for quite some time now. I certainly could afford to lose a few inches – and not just horizontally. Vertically. Most of my measurements are pretty much the same as they have been for years; it's simply that they now occur lower on my body.

My hips, for example, can be found somewhere around my knees, and my back end has begun to droop so seriously that sitting down has become a matter of merely backing up until my fanny meets the chair-seat.

Now, don't think for a single minute that any of this is my fault. It isn't. In the area of physical unfitness – as in so many other waddles of human life – women are the unwitting victims of a conspiracy so vast in its implications as to make Joe McCarthy's worst imaginings seem no more baroque than the arrangements for a surprise wedding shower.

As a matter of fact, in my breast pocket (now located in the vicinity of my stomach) I have documents which show, in specific detail, how the Workout Cult of the 1980s is a direct and deliberate offshoot of the Dessert Cult of the 1970s.

Oh my yes. You know what I'm talking about – the Dessert Cult, that spun-sugar web of sticky self-indulgence that gave rise to the establishment of desserts-only restaurants with names like Tout Sweet and Dessert Song. That hyperglycemic branch-plant of epicureanism which maintains stoutly (and I mean stoutly) that next to godliness comes not cleanliness, but Nanaimo bars, and that the highest aesthetic achievement, after Renaissance architecture, was the invention of Amaretto cheesecake.

Okay. So, many of us fell for it like a ton (and I mean a ton) of bricks. Which meant from there it was only a short, fat step to convincing us that our best remedy was not so much to diet as to exercise, because – and I quote – "Muscle weighs more than fat."

Muscle weighs more than fat. The catchiest lyric since "Moonlight Becomes You". I mean, it just kind of sings, doesn't it, with its level-headed promise that no matter what you eat and how much of it, it's going to be perfectly okay, because with the right exercise program you can convert it all into firmly contoured flesh? Right? Not quite.

What the workout enthusiasts often fail to point out is that while muscle may indeed weigh more than fat, key lime pie weighs more than anything. I know, because I'm wearing a slice of it on either hip, and even if I manage to convert it into muscle, my designer jeans are *still* going to look like riding jodhpurs.

But that niggling detail aside, the fact remains that the dessert-cult conspiracy, devil's-foodishly clever in design, is working. I've become one of those flabby statistics, just a girl who couldn't say no to the offer of another marron glacé for the road, and now I've got to pay the price.

Plus which, I'm dying to find out why my friend Yvonne is now wired on working out, to the point that she's had a personal phone installed down at her club, right next to the Pec-Deck, and in the rare moments when she's home, she keeps herself in trim by chinning herself on the roof of the carport and dead-lifting the Roto-Tiller.

The first thing I do is to throw a slightly musty long-sleeved black leotard (left over from an earlier adventure in humiliation at a Jazz Dance class) and a somewhat threadbare pair of dance-pants (left over from the same embarrassing era) into a shoulder bag (left over from an idealistic phase during which I erroneously believed buying a shoulder bag would induce me to tote my library books back on time; the proof of that fallacy is a copy of *Strangers on a Train* lying at the bottom of the bag, due back on September 23, 1966). The second thing I do is to arrive at the health club and immediately kick myself for having all The Wrong Stuff.

It's absolutely true. I look around me in the changing room – an overheated six-by-seven-foot space in which four hundred naked, sweaty women are attempting to squirm out of their street clothes and stow them in three hundred undersized dented lockers – and I perceive that nobody but nobody is suiting up for the class in an outfit that in any way resembles mine.

What's happened? What's happened, of course, in the intervening millennia since I quit that Jazz Dance class, disgusted with myself because I couldn't master the Flea-Hop, much less the more Byzantine intricacies of the Travelling Grapevine, is that exercise togs have become High Fashion, while my dowdy little dance ensemble has descended to a fashion level roughly the same altitude as my sagging bustline.

Worse than that, nobody seems to be porting their spiffy duds in shoulder bags any more. No way. Now the reticule of choice appears to be a businesslike little gym bag with valise-style handles to it, and some sort of sports-minded logo printed on the side, like "Adidas" – which, up until quite recently, I believed was what Spanish people said to each other when they meant goodbye.

Oh dear. How can I bring myself to produce that Bohemian-looking leotard from the absurdity of my shoulder bag? And what will ensue when those beat-up, no-longer-stretchy dance-pants come into full view? A chorus of hoots and jeers?

Not that my comrades-in-calisthenics appear to be hung up on the concept of unquestioning uniformity. Not at all. In fact, what characterizes their exercise attire is its infinite variety – almost infinite, that is. The only type of garb definitely not represented is the sort of sombre pseudo-arty outfit I have chosen.

We have, among other looks, the deliberately casual, consisting of a tee-shirt knotted at the waist (and we're dealing here with chicks whose waists are actually located at the midpoint of their bodies) and bearing a slogan like "It's Better in Borneo" to offer mute proof of the offbeat holidays its up-market owner is accustomed to enjoying. The tee-shirt is worn with bulky warm-up pants and is, I gradually deduce, the mode of dress in favor amongst those women who want the world to know they're at the club to work out, but do not wish to make any big deal about muscles.

For those to whom muscles are a very big deal indeed, there is the opportunity to show off burgeoning physiques in striped wrestling tops, dance-belts, and flesh-colored tights that give a general impression of a party of refugees from a trapeze act.

Then there are the dancer-types (Travelling Grapevine specialists, every one) who go in for pastel leg-warmers, bunched around their ankles for reasons that escape me, since if they were intended for use below the knee, wouldn't they be called ankle-warmers?

Finally, another major subgroup – loosely related to the dancer-types – are the model-types, perhaps the scariest of them all with their heart-stopping tallness and legs that appear to commence somewhere near their non-existent eyebrows. This is the group in the two-hundred-dollar rainbow-colored jumpsuits, to whom a Body-by-Gilda logo means as much as a Schiaparelli label once did to Paris mannequins. I find myself hating these women, and I like to think they might hate me too, if only they would give over their giraffe-like contemplation of the middle distance long enough to notice me somewhere down there around their kneecaps.

But this is the eerie thing. Nobody appears to notice anybody.

Women struggle out of their pantihose and into their Danskins like so many shedding snakes, bare buttock to bare buttock, silently meditative, as if they were at evening devotions in a cloistered order of nuns, rather than pressed up against dozens of their own naked kind in a steam-bath atmosphere faintly underscored by the pulsing disco rhythms seeping in from the workout room beyond.

In the end, it is this quality of self-absorbed obliviousness that furnishes me with sufficient courage to stake out a locker of my own and begin the process of changing into my absurdly out-of-sync workout attire, hopeful that if anybody *should* accidentally notice me at any point, they will merely assume I have come to give a reading of Beat poetry.

Unfortunately, finding myself out of my clothes proves to be just as depressing a circumstances as being found *in* them, since a covert survey of the change-room reveals that my naked body no more belongs in this high-style gathering than do my dowdy dance duds.

It's not just that I'm the only one in evidence who has underwear with "Thursday" embroidered on it (a Christmas present from a great-aunt, I swear it), it's also the fact that nobody else's elbows appear to have that mid-winter dried-apricot consistency that I simply took for granted as a part of life, like craggy knees and stretch-marked thighs. Come to think of it, nobody else exhibits those symptoms either, and the more peeks I sneak at the women around me, the more apparent it is that everyone else in the room served as a model for the Elgin Marbles.

Where do they get off, anyway, with those rounded contours, smooth shoulders, and unmarked pink-tinged skin? I mean, why the hell are these people bothering to take the time to work out, when as far as I can see, everything is already working out to perfection? My God, if these are examples of women who need to shape up, then obviously what *I* require is corrective surgery.

But, of course, I quickly recollect as we all pour out into the gym area for our aerobics class and our turn on the equipment that runs to huge sinister devices right out of a turn-of-the-century steam laundry, the goal here is not to be soft and round and pink. The goal is to be as hard and strong and straight-ahead as a streetcar, although, one hopes, with somewhat more allure.

The aerobics class, it goes without saying, is ghastly, and the

sleek pulchritude of the instructor is matched only by her psycho-
pathic brutality. "Press it out," she keeps saying, like a home ec
teacher giving a tutorial on ironing. "Press it out now." And
then – "Take it over the right leg now," "Take it all the way
down."

It? I'm sweating, gasping, listening fearfully for the telltale
sound of tearing ligaments that will surely result from the unnatural postures I am assuming. And yet I have sufficient presence of
mind to wonder – over the up-tempo din of some of the most
indecently peppy music I have ever heard – what is this "it" to
which the instructor continually refers?

Gradually, just before I black out from a muscle spasm, a
plausible answer dawns on me. "It" is nothing more or less than a
generalized and euphemistic term for the whole unsightly adipose
package our teacher is reluctant to cite by name. Understandably
so. I mean, I leave it to you: which sounds more inspirational –
"Press it out" or "Press out that ugly blubber"?

Ugly blubber somewhat pressed, if not exactly wrinkle-free, I
am then permitted to play among the machines, which turn out to
be far more fun than they look, even if every other woman in the
place – including a tiny transparent-looking Japanese lady –
seems capable of lifting three times as much weight as I am told is
my limit.

This is the moment at which I get some inkling of the routine to
which Yvonne (whom I have glimpsed on the other side of the
room, humming happily to herself as she performs cable cross-
overs) has become quietly addicted. I too experience the narcotic
rhythm of repeated motions, with much the same kind of mindless
pleasure I imagine a hamster must feel when running ceaselessly
in his little wheel. Every day, in every weigh, I'm getting stronger
and stronger.

For, of course, strong is the point of the story, and what began as
a desperate attempt to undo the havoc wrought by one too many
rhum babas has ended in a complete revolution in the requirements women have for their bodies. This fact is slowly beginning
to come clear to me, by the time I hang up my ankle-weights and
head back to the change-room to see what kind of chic outfits the
rest of the girls have brought to go home in.

To nobody's intense surprise (and nobody's interest, except

mine), in addition to sewing up the prize for Worst-Looking Workout Wear, it looks as though I have also managed to cop the highly coveted Frumpiest Togs To Go Home In Award, thanks to my choice of gardening pants and moth-eaten high school letter-sweater, while everyone else seems to be playing it safe by slipping into a little something they plan to wear over to Buckingham Palace later.

But none of that matters now, not since my heady discovery of the Joy of Pecs. Because I can see *very* clearly (at least, as clearly as the steamed-up change-room mirror permits) why Yvonne, and all these other women, and now I, have taken the road that leads away from petticoats toward pectorals, and how this muscular metamorphosis might ultimately transform the way we conduct almost every aspect of our lives.

Those tacky traditional female fight tactics – like refusing to explain what we are angry about, or snipping holes in his favorite socks – can give way to more straightforward expressions of displeasure, like drop-kicking his Datsun. Our old-fashioned methods of coping with unhappiness, such as spending our way out of a depression with the help of a credit card, can be replaced by healthy channels for despair, like pulling up Stop signs.

In fact, it seems as if a total change in attitude is already well under way, as I discover almost immediately after I've limped home on tender tendons and collapsed onto my bed. Lying on the end table beside me is a brand-new copy of *Gone With The Wind*, one of my favorite books of all time, which I have purchased on a whim in an updated and revised version, merely to investigate what changes have been made to what I have always regarded as impeccable text.

Eagerly (and yet at the same time attempting to avoid sudden movements) I snatch the book up and open it to the first page, having decided there is no time like the present to assess the extent of the literary damage. But, instead, what do I find to my enormous surprise, except that some sagacious editor has made the story of the coquettish Southern belle even *better* – if such a thing can be imagined – with a few judicious emendations, more in keeping with our brawn-conscious times.

For example, the first chapter still takes place on the front lawn of Tara, only now the vivacious young Scarlett successfully arm-wrestles both of the Tarleton twins. Later, at Twelve Oaks, when invited to "eat some barbecue", Scarlett misunderstands and instead eats the barbecue, brick by brick.

This is the same lively social occasion at which our plucky heroine first meets the reprobate Rhett Butler, who initially tries to tempt her virtue with a new line of leg-warmers he found up North, and then, when that ploy fails, promises to teach her everything she has ever wanted to know about anabolic steroids.

Scarlett's interest is piqued, but her chief allegiance is to the delicate and dreamy Ashley Wilkes, the only man in Georgia whose waist measurement is smaller than hers. Unfortunately, Ashley in his turn is infatuated with his cousin Melanie, for whom Scarlett has nothing but ill-concealed contempt, dismissing her as the type who probably thinks that Arnold Schwartzenegger is a cocktail made with Galliano.

Later, however, Scarlett comes to learn that she has badly underestimated Melanie, whose physical frailty is offset by a great heart that enables her to run up to four miles without any noticeable increase in pulse rate.

In spite of the grudging admiration Scarlett is eventually forced to show for the other woman, nothing can ease the perky belle's bitterness over the loss of her beloved Ashley to a rival. Scarlett continues to plan for the day when Ashley will come back to her, and one day as they split rails together (Ashley using an axe, Scarlett the edge of her hand), it comes out that Ashley does retain a certain amount of hidden ardor for her after all.

Nevertheless, Scarlett continues to run through other men (using a variety of long sharp objects), until she finally finds herself married to the handsome Captain Butler, no longer a blockade-runner since that embarrassing day when a blockade managed to outdistance him.

The couple settle in Atlanta, which has begun to rise again, particularly since Scarlett threw her shoulder under it, and all goes serenely enough until tragedy strikes their daughter, Brawny Blue, who is accidentally killed while attempting to bench-press her pony.

Nobody takes it harder than Rhett Butler – who dispatches the offending horse with a solid roundhouse right – but Scarlett hardly seems to notice the absence of her daughter, who had continually made a nuisance of herself by borrowing her mother's sweat pants – "just like Pa", as Scarlett was often wont to point out. Besides which, Scarlett's attentions are once again riveted on the vaporish Ashley Wilkes, whom she is once more determined to win.

However, somehow Ashley finds the strength to throw Scarlett over yet again, and this time she retaliates by throwing *him* over – right into a pitcher of mint juleps. Too late does Scarlett come to realize that it's Rhett she's really loved all this time. When she attempts to declare this to him, Rhett (by this time established in a new career as a hydro-electric engineer) tells her he frankly doesn't give a dam.

Heartbroken, but still determined to lure him back, Scarlett returns to Tara, has Nautilus equipment installed in the basement, and at the same time turns the main parlor into a desserts-only restaurant called The Yankee Desserter, with the idea of capitalizing on fitness and food, two of the most symbiotically connected fads of the day.

As to the question of whether Rhett Butler really will come back to her, Scarlett resolves to "think about that tomorrow". For, as she declares in the closing line of the book, "After all, tomorrow is another day, and muscle weighs more than fat."

Right on, Scarlett. So moved and excited am I by the revamped version of the story that, my aches and pains forgotten, I decide to leap up and call Yvonne to offer to lend it to her. But something – other than the agonized scream of mutilated flesh – stops me short. What if Yvonne doesn't like *Gone With The Wind*? I remember only too well what happened when Yvonne failed to enjoy a newly revised and muscle-bound copy of Louisa May Alcott's *Not So Little Women*.

She simply tore the book in half, hard covers and all.

Ask
Miss
Science

As usual this week, Miss Science's mailbag is full to bursting with eager questions from boys and girls on all kinds of subjects pertaining to the study of science.

Of course, Miss Science can't possibly be expected to publish all your letters, can she? So, this week, as always, she has made her selection on the basis of the most-frequently-asked-about subject.

Topping the list (far ahead of sex even, which ranked a lowly fifth this week – for shame, boys and girls, you're slipping) are inquiries from anxious young people who must have been reading their mummies' and daddies' newspapers or listening to the TV about the so-called Greenhouse Effect scientists warn us may soon be affecting life here on good old Mother Earth.

Miss Science wants to make it perfectly clear that you have nothing to fear from this phenomenon (my, that's a big word, isn't it?) and so she is taking good care to deal with all the questions you have sent in on this topic.

1) What exactly is the greenhouse effect?

That's for me to know and you to find out. (Ha ha. Just my little joke.) But seriously, the greenhouse effect is simply the warming of the earth's atmosphere that scientists tell us may begin to occur as the result of a toasty-warm blanket of carbon dioxide that is becoming thicker and thicker around the planet.

Well now, doesn't that sound all comfy and nice? Sort of like when your mummy tells you that you have to sweat out your cold in flannel pyjamas under the electric blanket. But where exactly did all that carbon dioxide come from, anyway, we'd like to know? From burning fossil fuels (you know what they are), that's where, and if this greenhouse-effect theory really does have any truth to it, by the end of the century, scientists tell us things are going to start getting awful peculiar around here, you bet.

2) What do you mean, peculiar?

Well, my goodness, use your head. If the earth's temperature starts rising, it's going to mean droughts in some areas, isn't it? And flooding in some others, as the ice all melts. And coastal areas submerged by rising oceans. And people reeling and staggering in the heat. And the –

3) Wah! I'm scared! I want my mummy!

Oh, for heaven's sake, now don't be such a baby. I told you it was only a theory, didn't I? Which means that it's not absolutely going to happen for sure for sure. Just probably. Which will be kind of too bad for you, boys and girls, won't it, since you're the ones who are really going to get it in the kishkas on this thing, while Miss Science and everybody else from her generation will be sleeping the sleep of the just. (You know what *that* means. Remember the week we discussed rigor mortis?)

4) What are we supposed to do, to make sure this greenhouse effect doesn't happen?

Well, goodness me, to be honest now, boys and girls, Miss Science doesn't see that there really is too much you *can* do. Because it certainly doesn't look as if the industrialized world is going to give up using fossil fuels, does it? And as long as that goes on, that blanket of nasty old CO_2 is going to get thicker and thicker and –

5) Miss Science, what do deer eat in the winter?

Not now, dear. Miss Science is still in the midst of answering another letter. Besides, I haven't even started to tell you about all the other results this greenhouse-effect business is going to have on everybody, even those of us right here in good old Canada, where hardly anything ever seems to happen – except in the apartment next door to Miss Science, that is, where it's party, party, party every night, and you wouldn't believe the kind of language that comes through my bedroom wall, so clearly that I hardly even need the glass up to my ear (you remember the week when I explained how that works) to hear it.

For example, if a country like ours starts to turn tropical all of a sudden, what's going to become of all that romantic snowbound isolation that has made us among the heaviest drinkers in the world? (Particularly in the apartment next door to Miss Science's.) And what about our distinctive pronunciations of words like "out" and "coast" that result from the pinching effect of almost perpetual frostbite on our lips? (No kidding, boys and girls, that's a scientific fact.)

Worst of all, what are other countries going to think of us when they can no longer pigeonhole us as "the white wilderness"? Americans won't be showing up at the border anymore with skis strapped to their roof racks in July, and we did so enjoy laughing about that.

And think of how much fun it's been to be criticized by the likes of Brigitte Bardot (no better than she should be, that one) and other foreigners, just because we happen to club baby seals to death. Once Canada warms up, all our fun will be spoiled, and we'll just have to wait for the seal pups to drop from heat prostration, won't we?

6) Miss Science, you're joking about this, aren't you?

Well, of course Miss Science is joking! There's no reason to take all this greenhouse-effect business seriously, because Miss Science knows better. In Miss Science's opinion, the scientific community has made an eensy-teensy little mistake in its calculations of the potential repercussions (look that word up yourselves; I'm sick of spoon-feeding you) of the coming warming trend.

I mean what these so-called men of science (and they are men, too, most of them) seem to assume is that the "warming" on the way is going to be of a purely literal nature. Meanwhile, it's my contention (and as a woman of science, I have a right to my opinions, although you'd never guess it from *them*) that what is actually going to happen is that the world will begin to warm *emotionally*, starting as soon as the beginning of the next decade, and stretching on into the twenty-first century.

The first changes we will notice will be among the traditionally frigid service occupations. Liquor store clerks will stop saying "What, you again?" in a loud voice as you approach the cash with your purchase. Gas station attendants will no longer expect you to pledge them your first-born child before they're willing to go near your windshield with a moist squeegee. And health food store owners will no longer put on expressions of outraged virtue every time you ask where they keep the cake mixes and the hot-dog buns.

Soon after that, even such hard-line emotional coldies as headwaiters and customs officials will begin to thaw, heralding the dawn of a whole new era of cordiality among strangers.

By the end of this century, Miss Science predicts, laughing and joking will be commonplace among passengers in elevators. Spontaneous sing-alongs will erupt on city buses, and formerly bleak and arid regions like dentists' waiting rooms and regional tax offices will be submerged in a tidal wave of *gemütlichkeit*.

And that's not all. In a general atmosphere of cosy well-being created by our ever snugger enveloping blanket of carbon dioxide, barbecues will start on the first try. Keys copied at the hardware store will actually fit the lock. Even the morning paper will land squarely on the porch step every morning.

Eventually, perhaps by the year 2100, slow golfers will regularly let better players go through; the phrase "hands-on" will have mercifully disappeared from the language; and when the movie *Rocky XI* is released, nobody will –

Ask Mr. Science

Well, it was quite disturbing news about our beloved Miss Science, wasn't it? But since her breakdown, she's been resting comfortably in a very pleasant and cheerful convalescent home, and I assure you that your many cards and gifts have been a real comfort to her, although whoever it was who sent along the atomizer filled with sulphuric acid really ought to seek some professional help.

Allow me to introduce myself. I'm Mr. Science, and from now on, I'm the one who will be addressing the pertinent scientific questions of the day by answering your letters. And just so we're absolutely straight about one thing – I had strictly nothing to do with the very sudden departure of Miss Science from the pages of this column, all right?

Like a lot of you science buffs out there, I had been reading her column faithfully since boyhood and while, in recent years, I'd begun to suspect that the old girl was doing much of her rowing with one oar out of the water, it was as great a surprise to me as it was to you when she started advancing truly crackpotted theories, like that whole unfortunate misunderstanding of what is meant by the greenhouse effect, and –

But look. What's past is past, right? And far be it from Mr. Science to cast aspersions on a colleague, or even to assign blame to the editors who really ought to have known better than to hire a woman for this job, particularly one whose entire background in the scientific arena consists of having once candled an egg back in the fifth grade.

Let me simply say, by way of suggesting a contrast to the *ancien régime* we have all so narrowly survived, that my credentials for this assignment include: practically a whole credit from a course in Technical Writing I took, and which I would have completed, had that not been the fall that I came down with mono; a certificate in Principles of Scientific Thought from a very reputable correspondence school that, I happen to know, only lost its accreditation as a result of a political coup on the Caribbean island on which it was located; and a third-place ribbon from the 1964 Oshawa Science Fair for outstanding proficiency in the egg-candling division. So there, Miss Science.

Having thus, I trust, established myself as the appropriately knowledgeable person for the job, let me now reach into my spiffy leather mailbag and find out what questions have been troubling my budding Edisons and aspiring Curies this week.

1) Can flowers actually communicate? My dad says you write like a pansy.

Oh, really, I won't even dignify that with a response. Except to comment that your father sounds very much to me like the sort of person who himself writes with all the intelligence and lyrical expressiveness of a trash-compacter.

2) How come trains have separate washrooms for men and women, while planes don't?

Good Lord. Is this the kind of thing you waste your time wondering about? In fact, nobody knows why trains need gender-specific rest-room facilities, although in all likelihood the concept was pioneered by the same engineering Einstein who designed the subway system so that one may ride the escalator down, but is obliged to walk up.

Actually, when you stop to think about it, our world is positively overrun with structural absurdities of this sort, and perhaps your question is, therefore, not quite as inane as I initially thought.

Why do we need access to 180 television channels, for instance, when there's nothing to watch on any of them? Why was all the parking space put out in the suburbs instead of downtown where we could really use it? Why do people spend forty bucks having all the hair clipped off their poodle, and then have to shell out another twenty-five for a little wool jacket to keep the creature warm? Above all, what's the point of converting temperatures into Celsius unless we have plans to export our weather to Europe?

3) How could you take the sole means of livelihood away from a poor defenceless middle-aged woman?

Tut, tut, Miss Science – disguise your handwriting next time you write in with a heart-rending reproach, if you expect it to be taken seriously. As I've already explained most patiently to the boys and girls, your mind has been highwire-walking for quite some time without a net, and it really was a case of being cruel to you only to be kind.

May I remind you, Miss Science, that recent specious assertions of yours that have graced this column include your explanation that "thermal expansion" refers to the way long underwear eventually begins to bag around the knees and the rear end, your insistence that atoms were first smashed by Galileo, who dropped them to the ground from the top of a tower, and, of course, your legendary recapitulation of the life cycle of the dragonfly from its infancy in its mother's pouch, through its being pushed from the nest as soon as its feathers have sprouted, to its adult life in the clover fields, gathering pollen, and ultimately on to its glorious transformation into a caterpillar.

Really, Miss Science. If I were you, I'd count myself lucky to have escaped legal proceedings instituted on behalf of poor abused Mother Nature!

4) Please explain to me the goals of the current U.S. and Soviet space missions. I need this information for a school project.

At last, at last, a question with a little meat on its bones, although I must say I can't wholeheartedly condone the practice of relying on others to furnish you with material for your school assignments.

Nevertheless, one valid approach I would suggest you might take to the question is to attack it from the point of view of relative technologies, as the United States in recent years appears to be slanting the thrust of its rocketry toward information-gathering processes based upon –

Ask Miss Science

Well, well, well. The tables certainly have turned sharply once more, haven't they, boys and girls? (You remember that table-turning was dealt with some months back in my column on Voodoo, Spells, and Other Useful Branches of the Vengeful Sciences.)

I must say it's fascinating to see how some people climb all over themselves in their haste to profit on another's temporary misfortunes. But now, I'm glad to say, God's back in his heaven, and the enemy has been thoroughly routed.

To the many of you who addressed letters of complaint and indignant phone calls to the offices of the editor, demanding that I be given back my job, my grateful thanks. To those few of you who sided with the interloper and placed their bets on the forces of darkness – better luck next time.

Not that there is going to be a next time. Miss Science is firmly back in the saddle and riding the range of scientific know-how once more. As for that snide little weasel who tried to steal my column out from under me, and whose unsavory sexual proclivities were so accurately pinpointed by the father of one of my – oh well.

Now pupils...the very first thing Miss Science intends to do (after she rubs a little more healing salve on those nasty acid burns she sustained from a certain booby-trapped atomizer, and has a brief chat with a very nice young man named Rocco who is working on discovering the identity of the culprit) is to pick up the column exactly where it was dropped last week, after the sudden and not at all regrettable departure of its recent incumbent.

The question, I believe, was connected to the Russian and American space efforts, and what I would like to advise the boys and girls right off the bat is to give the whole thing as little credence as possible. Myself, I went entirely off it all back in the fifties, when the Russians shot the poor little doggie off into space, made us all fall in love with him, then announced they had no plans to bring him back.

The moon shot by the Americans in 1969, as I'm sure you boys and girls realize, was rigged. When that Neil Armstrong person stepped out onto the lunar landscape, there was a tiny blurry little road sign visible in one corner of the TV screen that said "Last Chance to Get Gas Before the Desert". Now I ask you. What kind of gullible fools do they take us for?

And, of course, when it comes to the terminology, anybody can see these people (mostly men, it goes without saying) really have to work at making everything sound so mysterious and complicated. Nice straightforward words like "Yes" get turned into "Affirmative" and "That's a Roger". (Besides which, it's not a Roger. In my day, when the moon hit your eye like a big pizza pie, *that* was a Roger.)

Interestingly enough, even taking into account their shaky command of the English language, the Russians do a lot better in the terminology department. For instance, what about that nice word "cosmonaut" that gives you a picture of some globe-trotting sophisticated *bon vivant*. While the Americans are stuck with "astronaut", suggestive of absolutely nothing except some Hawaiian-shirted suburbanite whose lawn is seeded with artificial turf.

And then, of course, the Russians do so awfully well naming their space vehicles such adorably whole-grain names, like Salyut, and Soyuz – which sounds to Miss Science exactly like some kind of nutritional supplement – and then on the other hand, there are the Americans with those ridiculously boastful names like Apollo and Challenger and...

Career Costuming

As someone whose personal wardrobe decisions begin and end with, "Should I wear jeans or go naked?" I've always assumed that I'm basically unqualified to make definitive statements about fashion.

Lately, however, I've begun to rethink that position. I mean, surely a world in which the Pope talks knowledgeably about birth control and Pentagon spokesmen claim to be experts on peace can also accommodate the sartorial opinions of a self-confessed frump?

Besides which, as the lifestyle (formerly women's) page in the newspaper tells us over and over, high fashion just ain't what it useta be – by which I assume they mean snide, snotty, and dictatorial. Which is really rather too bad in a way, since I used to look forward to those shrill injunctions from Paris every spring, telling us to mix it, match it, raise it, lower it, belt it, bolero it, buckle it, bare it, tie it, and stuff it. Not that I ever obeyed any of these commands, mind you. But I did look forward to them.

Now, though (if you can believe what you read in the paper), everything's different, and if you want to put on a torn tee-shirt, add to it corrective shoes and a section of chain-link fence worn as a miniskirt, that's perfectly okay, while for more formal occasions earrings may be added with a staple gun.

On the other hand, it's equally okay to be seen in a tailored tweed jacket and oxfords that a Kremlin file clerk would reject as too severe, or a nostalgic shirtwaist and frothy crinoline straight out of *Where the Boys Are*.

All of which would be fine and dandy with me, of course, if it were only a matter of peeking into the closet and deciding on an outfit. But it's not. Instead, you must decide on a "look".

Now, look. Personally, I couldn't care less whether I have a definite look or not. Just so long as I don't have a definite smell. But if you *are* in the business of trying to choose whether to allow your image to be derived from Hollywood of the forties, or inspired by a multiple-vehicle collision, it could get confusing, couldn't it?

Not to mention onerous, considering how many of these so-called looks involve selecting an entirely new personality for yourself upon which you can build a wardrobe.

Let's be clear about one thing here. I'm not just talking about what shows to the world at large. I'm talking from the ground up, all right? Don't even begin to worry yet who you're going to impersonate out there on the street. Who do you plan to be on your way from your bureau to your closet? In other words, let's be aware of underwear.

One currently popular option in the underwear department is the sleazy trollop look, and you really should consider it. Unfortunately, it's going to mean donning something you thought, when you threw it away twenty years ago, you would never have to think about again. No, I'm not referring to your goals, ideals, or moral principles. What I'm talking about is your garter-belt.

No kidding. The garter-belt is suddenly very big again, which is kind of depressing news for those of you who got tired of going for tetanus shots every time the metal suspender fasteners bit into the tender flesh at the back of your thigh.

But hey, garter-belts are sexy, right, and with that recommendation, fear of sepsis goes right out the window. Not to mention concern for personal comfort and the understandable desire to avoid the aggravation of stocking tops that inevitably quit approximately two inches before the garter-snaps begin.

Still and all, if you really can't face the prospect of yelping in pain every time you sit down, or marking the passing of the hours by how many degrees your stockings have twisted, be of good cheer. There's another underwear look that might reflect you to a T – or, better yet, might reflect the somebody far more interesting and worthwhile that your mother, husband, and best friends still cherish furtive hopes of your yet becoming.

This is the "Lady Equality" look, epitomized by a line of jockey and boxer shorts for women that some designers have recently put on the market, perhaps merely in a spirit of idle curiosity to see just how absurd their ideas have to get before women will begin to suspect they are being groomed as potential copy for future instalments of "Ripley's Believe It Or Not".

Because what I really think I have to mention, just to make it absolutely clear what weird countryside we're wandering through here, is that these jockey and boxer shorts for women come with a fly opening.

Uh-oh. Now don't tell me we came all this way with Betty Friedan, *Ms.* magazine, and the principle of equal pay only to find out that Freud was right after all. Could it be that fashion has recognized what we've been too blind to see, which is that what we've *really* wanted all this time has been nothing more or less than the thing that men have that enables them to rule the world – jockey shorts with a fly? Could be.

An even more intriguing question, for my money, is what further look might be created through combining macho unmentionables with the silk-stocking revival, by inviting women to wear their garter-belts under their jockey shorts. They could call it the "Corporate Concubine Look".

If, however, you regard the entire subject of look-oriented lingerie as simply too frivolous to even bother discussing, then you may just be ready to graduate to some career-minded outer wear, in which case, may I suggest something in the medical line? You'd better act quickly, though. Medicine is a highly competitive profession, and already hospital linen services have begun complaining loudly about the high incidence of theft that has resulted from the growing trendiness of hospital greens.

Just for the record, hospital greens are not the wilted beans and watery spinach so prominently featured on every patient's meal tray. Nor are they an allusion to the golf courses upon which doctors can be frequently found, performing delicate and skilful operations when they really should be back in the O.R., botching up some surgery.

No. What is being referred to here is the green surgical coveralls that have become all the rage as lounge wear in the non-medical world. Why? Probably the loose-limbed savoir-faire of the medicos on old *M*A*S*H* reruns has something to do with it. Or a complicated carry-over from blissful childhood recollections of illicit games of Doctor. Or is it simply that hospital greens provide the unique opportunity of allowing under-achievers to dress for a higher tax bracket without having to brave the scorn of the sales staff in the snootier stores?

Whatever the reason, I have to admit I'm a little worried about the effect that all this Career Costuming is going to have on our daily lives. Those women who take up black lace garter-belts for instance – are they going to start believing their own slutty press? Will previously responsible, right-thinking wives and mothers gradually find themselves hanging around ill-lit doorways in a provocative way? Addressing the men who pass by as "honey" or "sailor"? Sleeping in till noon, then clattering around the rest of the day in high-heeled mules and a silk kimono? Badgering servicemen for stockings?

And what about those persons of either sex whose wardrobes begin to lean heavily toward hospital greens? I'd hate to think they're going to start disappearing mysteriously from the office on Wednesday afternoons. Or getting into the habit of barging on and off elevators ahead of everyone else. Or disturbing the rest of us in the theatre when their telephone-pager goes off. Or prefacing explanations with "Let me put this as simply as I can...." Or – worst of all – coming out with a diet book.

The considerations begin to take on a truly grim aspect when you come to tally up how many other kinds of job-related looks there are out there on the street. How about, for example, all those cute little kids running around in soldiers' camouflage attire? Am I going to wake up some morning to discover that my neighborhood is being pacified by a battalion of Grade Fours with orders to kill? Or happen to pass by the schoolyard and notice that the playground has been reorganized for tank manoeuvres? Or encounter my next-door neighbor in tears because her ten-year-old has been sent on peacekeeping duty in Cyprus?

This, I feel with a dreary sense of certainty in the pit of my stomach, is only the beginning of a burgeoning and dangerous trend. More and more people are going to start dressing in career costumes, not only as a way of acting out wistful fantasies, but also in order to emulate professions that enjoy a particularly prestigious profile in today's appearance-oriented society.

In which case, we should be prepared to pick out the impersonators from the true practitioners. To that end, I have taken the liberty of drawing up a short introductory list of the most frequently mimicked professions, with tips on how to detect the dilettantes, which I present for your consideration.

Watch out for individuals costumed as:

1) Owners of pasta bars – This look is easily created by knotting a sweater loosely around the neck, slathering one's face in a thick layer of Man Tan, showing a lot of chest hair, and wearing a single earring shaped like a manicotto. Both authentic and bogus pasta-bar owners refer to all fattening food as "wicked", but you can pick out the impostor when you phone up for a reservation and he says it's no problem. A real pasta-bar owner is always full up at least a week ahead, and refuses to take reservations for parties of fewer than eight.

2) Entertainment lawyers – Expect practitioners of this extremely trendy branch of the law to be emulated by laymen who will don the distinctive costume of the profession, which combines the traditional barrister's wig with leg-warmers and tap shoes. You can spot the phony, though, if he fails to use the word "prior" when he means "before".

3) Restaurant critics – This is a profession to which individuals who crave to be both hated and feared gravitate after they have failed to pull off their imitation of Hitler. It's tricky trying to sort out the wheat and the chaff here, since even authentic restaurant critics tend to look like frauds, as a result of the necessary anonymity of their calling, which prompts the widespread use of slouch hats, false beards, and fake noses. In the end, it's the expression of permanent disdain that hallmarks the genuine article. That, and the real pleasure they appear to get from being accosted by an angry pasta-bar owner screaming at them, "I'll have you know our *linguine vongole* is the best in town. How dare you say it has 'all the texture and savor of boiled erasers'?"

Of course, right about now, you may be harking back to my opening remarks on the subject of fashion, and recalling that I was quite frank in my admission that I know nothing about it. Why, then, should you now heed my caveats and dire predictions about the possible future course fashion may take? Simple. Because I've got good instincts.

Let me put it another way. When considering the possibility of whether it will rain tomorrow, who are you more likely to believe: the weatherman who says no, or your bunion that aches like the dickens?

Yeah, I figured. So just think of me as your aching bunion. And remember you heard it here first.

Funny, You Don't Look Kiddish

It seemed that whomever I approached on the subject, the response was always the same. Starting with my favorite drama teacher and trusted mentor, Miss Kipley.

"Miss Kipley," I said, "I've made an important decision. I want a career in show business."

The old lady gave me a wary sideways look. "You're kidding."

"No, I'm not. Why – don't you think I have what it takes to make it?"

"No," said Miss Kipley, after a pause. "Frankly, I don't."

"But. . . you told me I reminded you of a young Hepburn."

"Mitchell Hepburn," said Miss Kipley quickly. "Former Premier of the Province of Ontario."

"Oh. I – I see."

At my evident distress, her expression softened. "Oh, what the heck. All right, maybe I *did* say you have some of the qualities of Kate Hepburn as she was in the old days. Maybe you *do* have the stuff, but. . . well, there's something else."

"Something else? That I'm missing, you mean? What? Miss Kipley, tell me. What is it?"

"I can't tell you," she said, with a strange look around her mouth. "You'll have to find it out for yourself."

I tried to talk it over with my therapist, kindly but eccentric Dr. Fleischschmerz, but didn't get much farther.

"My mind's made up," I said. "I belong in the theatre."

"Ah," said Dr. Fleischschmerz ambiguously.

"What is that 'ah'? Ah good or ah bad?"

"Bad, if you want to know the truth. I see big problems ahead."

"You sound like my drama coach, Miss Kipley. But she wouldn't tell me what the problem was."

"You don't say."

"Well? Aren't *you* going to let me in on it?"

"So – " exclaimed Dr. Fleischschmerz abruptly, seizing his notepad and pencil, "had any good dreams lately? That one last week, where you are chased around the Clock Room in the British Museum by the chorus from *Turandot*, all brandishing egg timers, was a real dilly. Got another one like that, by any chance?"

"Dr. Fleischschmerz, I demand to know why you won't tell me what's standing between me and a successful show business career."

"Some things a person has to find out for himself."

"If that's true, then what am I coming here for?"

"Because Dr. Kreike didn't have any hours free, and my office was right next door."

I gasped at his perspicacity. "How on earth did you know that?"

"It was all there," Dr. Fleischschmerz shrugged modestly. "In the dream."

At that point, I decided there were some things a person had to find out for himself.

My first task as a show business hopeful was to get myself an agent, which is how I wound up in the offices of O'Connor and Farentino Artists' Representatives, chatting to Augie Farentino and showing him my résumé and photos.

"Terrific," he said. "Beautiful. What can I tell you? So all right, already. We got a deal here, am I right? I'm in for ten per cent of the whole schmeer."

"The whole what?"

"Oi, gevalt. What are we talking here?"

"Mr. Farentino, I wish I knew. I can't make out what you're saying. Look – I – uh – speak a little Italian. Would that make it easier for you?"

"Italian, schmitalian. Who needs it? Look, don't make such a megillah here. This is O'Connor, my partner and nexdoorekeh."

Rory O'Connor bounded into the room, like a leprechaun with a medallion, and proffered a freckled hand for me to shake. "What, don't tell me my cockamamy partner here is giving you tsuris. Such a schmegegge you don't need, am I right?"

I decided right there and then that I would make my entrance into the business without benefit of artistic representation.

The first gig I managed to land for myself was on the same bill as a nervous comic from Kapuskasing named Sandy McCutcheon.

"Look, don't worry from the audience, faygeleh," he told me right off the bat. "I'll spritz a little with them first, get the schmaltz going and then – "

"Pardon?" I said.

"No burtching, now," McCutcheon cautioned. "You're gonna do sensational. Not like that bulbenik who useta open for me one time – such a pisk you never saw."

In confusion, I began to cry, and McCutcheon had me fired on the spot. Still, I managed somehow to remain convinced that my experiences thus far represented nothing more than a brief run of random ill-luck. God knows how long it would have taken me to realize the truth, had I not had a chance encounter on the street with Bronwen Llewellyn, an old classmate from theatre school days, whose career was reputedly thriving.

"Bronwen!" I exclaimed, hugging her gratefully. "It's so nice to see a friend."

"You think by me it's no big deal? Nu, so are we going some place for a nosh and a schmooze, or what?"

"Bronwen," I said soberly over a cup of tea and a bran muffin, "you've changed somehow."

She looked up from slathering cream cheese on her bagel. "What are you talking?"

"No, it's what *you're* talking that has me confused. Back in theatre school, I don't remember you sprinkling so much Welsh into your conversation."

"Welsh? What are you, meshugge?"

It was only then that I began to really grasp the problem. What Miss Kipley had been unable to bring herself to mention; the embarrassing difficulty that not even Dr. Fleischschmerz had been frank enough to articulate. The plain and simple fact of the matter was that the *lingua franca* of show business was Yiddish. And I couldn't understand a word of it.

"Oh my God," I moaned to Bronwen, "what am I going to do?"

"Here, have a shtikl bagel," she said soothingly. "And don't be farchadat. You – " Suddenly recalling the nature of my problem,

Bronwen caught herself up short, then began again in English. "You'll learn it, like the rest of us. It's easy."

Some easy. Thinking I could patch things up with McCutcheon the comic, I invited him to lunch for the next day, then spent the rest of the afternoon with a Yiddish-English dictionary.

In the restaurant, I told him he was, by all accounts, a very big mamzer in show business. Whereupon McCutcheon decorated my lap with the contents of his soup plate. Only when I got home and checked with the dictionary did I perceive my mistake. The word I'd been searching for was macher, and considering that I'd called him a bastard, I counted myself lucky that McCutcheon hadn't been dining on molten lead.

Only slightly daunted in my fence-mending mission, I took myself back downtown to O'Connor and Farentino, Artists' Representatives, to see whether I could do a better job of communicating with them this time around. Plainly hopeful, they offered me some wine to patch things up, but when I lifted my glass and said, "Mah-jong!" O'Connor and Farentino exchanged a quick glance, then blurted in chorus that they were sorry, but they'd suddenly remembered that their client roster was full after all, and they couldn't take me.

As pleased as I was to have actually understood one of their utterances in its entirety, I was nevertheless completely dejected by this fresh evidence of my failure to master even a single phrase of Yiddish. What was going to happen to my career?

Sadly, I trudged home to my underheated one-room flat, where I was being threatened with eviction because, apparently, the cockroaches counted as pets, which were strictly forbidden by the lease. Absently tossing a small ball for one of the roaches to fetch, and waiting for another to bring me the evening paper and my slippers, I began to ponder seriously whether I really had a vocation in the entertainment field.

Learning Yiddish was plainly out of the question for a dunce like me. On the other hand, without it, what hope did I have of convincing anyone that I could communicate in the arcane terminology of my chosen profession? Worst of all, why was it that so many other goyim – McCutcheon, Bronwen, the two agents – had acquired the knack, and I couldn't?

It was in that moment, at the blackest ebb of a dark and

desperate hour, that a solution came to me. If I couldn't master Yiddish, I would simply learn to fudge it, by devising a made-up language of my own – called Kiddish.

From that day forward, my fortunes took a one-hundred-and-eighty-degree turn for the better. By rifling a standard English dictionary, I managed to compile a varied list of words that sounded vaguely Yiddish – at least in spirit – and I began to employ them at every opportunity.

"Snooze", for example, is the sort of word that, although of unknown origins, has a nice show-biz ring to it. Therefore, I let it be known that, every afternoon between two and four, I was unavailable for appointments on account of I was taking a snooze.

"Mooch", as far as I was concerned, was every bit as denigrating as schlemiel and schnorrer; so I made it a staple of my derogatory vocabulary. Then there was "snog" (British for kiss), and "stooge" and "nudge", as well as – best of all – "bodge", a maverick word I resuscitated from my days in the schoolroom, where, as children, the frequently voiced complaint was, "Teacher, he bodged my arm while I was writing."

Once my conversation had been liberally peppered with these auditorially satisfying syllables, I became bolder and more experimental, devising completely new words in the Kiddish mode with which to astound both friends and business connections.

"Picknik", for instance, became my home-grown term for someone excessively critical and fussy. In deference to the French fact, I came up with "pontiff" as a word to describe a bridge enthusiast.

Taking my cue from such Yiddish-Americanisms as "donstairsikeh" (a downstairs neighbor), I was able to explain to all and sundry that "Erikeh" described a person often found daydreaming in the ether, while a "chic-seh" was a non-Jewish woman with good clothing sense.

Finally, by the time I was playing Carnegie Hall on a regular basis (having long since cashiered O'Connor and Farentino in favor of a Broadway hotshot named Gonzalez who referred to someone as a mensch at least once in every paragraph) I had developed my Kiddish lexicon to the point that I even had a word – "crocker" – to describe a cook who favored pre-packaged mixes, as well as the expression "lavish" for someone passionately devoted to washing.

Someone who has taken almost as keen a pleasure as I have in my phenomenal show business success is dear old Dr. Fleischschmerz, whom I always drop in on for a sort of psychological fine-tuning every time I'm back in town.

"Anyway," I remarked to him on my last visit, "I guess you were right after all. Some things a person just has to work out for himself."

"Who said such a stupid thing? I did?"

"Yes, don't you remember? Instead of telling me outright that I'd have career problems because of my failure with Yiddish, you let me discover it for myself."

"Gott im Himmel!" declared Dr. Fleischschmerz, smiting his brow in astonishment. "Yiddish? What do I know from Yiddish? The thing I didn't want to tell you was you were never gonna make it in theatre with a voice like that. Frankly, you couldn't carry a tune in a bucket."

"Dr. Fleischschmerz, I'm not a singer."

"You're telling me. What did I say? But better you should find it out for yourself, hein?"

On my way out the door, I came up with the perfect Kiddish word to describe Dr. Fleischschmerz, a word that also translates perfectly into both the English and the Yiddish languages. The problem was it isn't printable in any of them, so I can't tell you what it is. Which is probably just as well. Some things a person has to find out for himself.

A Cat's Guide to Woman Care

So. You've decided to take a woman into your home. Wise choice, for when all is said and done, a woman makes the ideal housepet for any cat. While men are inclined to be noisy, in need of constant attention, and liable to shed their coats all over the furniture, women are singularly able to amuse themselves when left alone for prolonged periods, handle their own basic grooming requirements, and adapt easily to the constraints of urban life.

Even cats who start out as lukewarm woman owners gradually become more and more attached to their pets, and some come almost to believe that these lovable creatures are capable of independent thought.

Ridiculous, you might say – and perhaps you'd be right. But one thing is for certain: the more understanding you show your female pet, the more she'll reward you with her simple devotion. Just as long as you make sure she knows who's in charge, by following these few basic tips on Woman Care:

Number One. Don't Let Her Become Finicky About Her Food. Although once essentially a meat-and-potatoes eater, modern domesticated woman no longer dines with the straightforward gusto of her forebears. She is quite likely to turn up her nose at anything she regards as "high calorie" and will virtually starve herself for weeks at a time on a regime of 2 per cent cottage cheese, Stouffer's Lean Cuisine, and bottle upon bottle of Ramlösa, all in the name of "getting back into those Alfred Sung pants that cost me a month's salary last fall".

As her owner, you must not allow this to happen. For one thing, when she dines like an inmate of a Dickensian workhouse, so do you. Lean Cuisine and cottage cheese offer little in the way of succulent scraps, and if there breathes a cat with soul so dead that he can stomach the taste of mineral water, I have yet to meet him.

Of more significance, however, is the fact that a hungry pet is a bad-tempered pet, as you will discover round about the third day of one of her scorched-earth fasts. Previously lovable traits of yours, like napping on her black velvet cape, will be met with shrieks of disapproval, while the most touching display of affection – such as leaping onto her naked shoulder as she applies her mascara – will elicit expletives she could only have picked up in a former life as a ticket-taker in a bear pit.

Far better for her (and, not incidentally, for you) is the alternative of avoiding the necessity of such temperament-eroding abstinences in the first place, which is what the next pointer is all about.

Number Two. Keep Her Well-Exercised. Since bending over and straightening up have been well established as the perfect calisthenics to counter waistline bulge (a common affliction in domesticated female humans), you owe it to your pet to keep her slim and trim by encouraging her to bend often to fill your food dish with delectable snacks.

Or, as an additional inducement to exercise, try knocking small objects – such as earrings, lipstick cases, and perfume stoppers – down from her vanity table onto the floor, where they will inevitably come to rest behind a table leg, under the edge of the rug, or down the heating vent – all ideal localities to inspire your woman to healthy gymnastic contortions as she attempts to retrieve her lost treasures.

Of course, the upper arm of the female human is an area much in need of continual flexion in order to keep it firm and supple. Help out in this regard by rubbing up affectionately against her leg as a means of prompting her to exercise her arm through repeatedly applying a clothes-brush to the numerous hairs you've deposited on her wool slacks.

Walking, experts in the field of human anatomy tell us, is the best all-round exercise there is. Be a responsible pet owner by ensuring that your woman is walked thoroughly and often. One recommended method is to meow at her as a signal to let you out, then several minutes after she has done so, ask to come back in. After another few moments, demand once more to go outside, and so forth.

You'll be amazed, not only at how often this gullible creature is willing to trot back and forth to the door, but also at how many miles of hardwood she will have covered by the time she actually drops from exhaustion.

Number Three. Take an Interest in Her Work. There's nothing the typical female pet takes more seriously these days than her career – with the possible exception of men (see Number Five below). In her zeal to rise up the success ladder, your pet will often feel it necessary to bring work home of an evening or on weekends. Here's where you can really help out.

If she's supposed to be working on a report, but seems creatively blocked, why not leap up onto the typewriter keys and tap out the first few characters for her? Where writing is concerned, getting started is often the hardest part, and perhaps all she really needs is someone to overcome the Blank Piece of Paper Syndrome for her.

When she spreads out charts and graphs on the table, tunnel under them in a playful way. After all, there's more to life than blind ambition, and why is she living with a cat in the first place if not to have some fun?

Above all, do not allow her to tire herself out through prolonged periods of uninterrupted concentration on closely worded documents. As soon as you decide she's had enough, settle yourself down smack on top of whatever it is she's reading. Although her initial reaction to this manoeuvre may not be entirely positive, persist in the assurance that some day she'll thank you.

Number Four. Treat Any Ailments Immediately. Although the female housepet is essentially a robust creature – as demonstrated by her ability to stay awake for up to ten hours at a stretch without so much as one tiny catnap – you must bear in mind that her system is complex, and therefore susceptible to ailments of many arcane types that you must be able to recognize and deal with.

One common illness is something she calls "the blahs". This affliction usually comes on very suddenly and inexplicably; it can be brought on by something as apparently harmless as a phone call (or the *lack* of a phone call – female pets are notoriously indiscriminate about embracing arbitrary pretexts for disgruntlement).

How do you know for sure if your pet has a case of the blahs? Simple. She will tell you. Over and over. Until, eventually, you find yourself sorely tempted to get out of earshot by seeking refuge on the top shelf of that linen closet you've been intending to check out for some time anyway.

However, if felinely possible, you must resist the siren song of that closet, because this is a moment when your poor helpless woman needs an owner's loving ministrations.

It won't be easy, of course. Dealing with sickness never is. You will be forced to endure being clutched tightly – even moistly – and crooned to in a fashion that borders, quite frankly, on the moronic.

Worse than that, you will be compelled to hear again and again, in a tone too mournful to describe, her repeated assertions that you are "so lucky to be just a cat".

Just a cat. In the face of this inanity you must, of course, strive not to lose your temper. Remember that you simply cannot expect a mere human to comprehend the multifarious responsibilities of your complicated life, which include recalling which sofa cushion it was that you left your mouse under, and deciding on an alternative lavatory site when your litterbox gets too full.

Do not, by the way, confuse the blahs with "the blues", because the latter can be much more easily treated. By and large, the blues is a minor ailment your pet may have contracted in any number of ways, including looking over her old high school yearbook, discovering an enlarged pore, or receiving her monthly statement from the credit card people.

If you suspect your pet is suffering from the blues – telling you that you're "lucky to be just a cat" can be a symptom here too – merely choose a conspicuous portion of the living-room carpet and roll over on your back, with your paws tucked up comically under your chin. (Under no circumstances should you omit the paws; they are the element that really makes this stunt.)

Immediately, your pet will be capsized by delighted laughter, and will kneel down on the rug to give you an appreciative chest rub, her case of the blues all but forgotten.

Number Five. Let Her Mate, But Not Too Often. As important as the male of the species may be to her (and don't kid yourself, she thinks they're vital), your pet must be made aware, right from the outset, that, while these bozos may come and go (mostly they go), *you* are the real emotional constant in her life.

The first time a prospective beau drops around, check him out to determine whether he's a Stud or a Stayer. If he looks like the former, you're in luck. The Stud type is only in it for the short haul, and any hint of impending permanence will send him scurrying.

Do your part to get him out the door by leaping into his lap and staring up into his face with a worshipful "Are you my new Daddy?" expression in your eyes. Fetch the pair of bedroom slippers left over from the last boyfriend you got rid of. Draw his attention to the album of family photos on the bookcase.

After an hour of this kind of effusive treatment, the Stud is guaranteed to be on his feet, glancing at his watch, and feigning sudden recollection of another pressing appointment.

The Stayer, on the other hand, is a tougher nut to crack, and you must be aware that you are dealing with someone who intends to supplant you in your pet's affections – probably kicking you out of the brocaded armchair in the bargain.

Suck up to the interloper while your pet is watching; wait until she has left the room before you snag his silk socks. Above all, time this manoeuvre so that the Stayer can be caught in the act of kicking you away precisely as your pet returns.

To drive the wedge further between the two lovebirds, underscore your pet's shortcomings in the domestic sphere by producing dust-bearded toffees (secreted by you weeks earlier against just such an emergency) from under the sofa, and batting them around conspicuously in front of the guest. Or else rummage the garbage for discarded convenience-food packets, and lay them at his feet with the respectful air of a prosecuting attorney entering an exhibit for the Crown.

If all that should fail, it's time to bring out the big guns. Sit on the bed staring at him disconcertingly, preferably at a crucial moment in the romantic proceedings. Continue your unblinking surveillance as he steps out of the shower, naked and vulnerable. Finally, indicate the conclusions of your intense observation by bringing up your dinner on the chair where his folded clothes are lying.

Be warned, however, that any Stayer who survives these tactics is made of stern stuff and is therefore liable to become part of your life. In which case you must learn to treat him exactly as you do your own pet: ignore him completely unless he has a can-opener in his hand, or a cup of scalding coffee on his knee.

Of course, if he eventually takes a notion to move into the abode of you and your pet, then you've got the infinitely more complicated problem of multiple pet ownership to deal with.

Number Six. Make Sure the New Addition Knows Who's Boss. *You* are, naturally, and if your new pet fails to grasp that fact right at the outset, you have only yourself to blame for the conse-quences. As previously explained, a man makes a somewhat more problematic housepet than a woman, but with firm handling and the patience of an angel, some gratifying results can be achieved.

Certainly there's no reason on earth that your new male can't be trained to obey many of the same simple commands as your female does, with almost as much comprehension and alacrity.

The first thing that must be impressed upon him, quite abso-lutely, is the importance of serving up your meals on time – particularly in the morning. To this end, give him some broad hints well in advance of the actual event by – for instance – hopping up onto the bed to tread gently on his larynx at 5 a.m., as a reminder that breakfast is a scant three hours away.

As an added measure, and in order to make the further point that continual underfeeding has already had serious repercus-sions on your health, sneeze wetly in his sleeping face.

Another lesson that must be taught immediately to this new addition to the family hearthside is that he should not expect to have your female pet all to himself. Ever. Make it a habit to insert yourself between them on the couch when you notice them watching television together in a way that looks too suspiciously companionable. Or, when romance is in the air, frolic among the bedsheets with them, sinking your claws playfully into whatever random expanses of flesh become exposed to you in the melee. Lastly, make sure that the boundary lines of your territorial imperative have been clearly drawn for your male pet, in order to kibosh quickly the gradual encroachments he will otherwise begin to make on your space. For instance, you may overhear him suggest to your female that the spare room would make an excellent study for him, provided that your litterbox is removed from it.

"Spare room" indeed. Here is a pet who needs to be taught a lesson in rightful ownership, since he has clearly failed to recognize whose claim it is that has already been staked on the terrain in question. By all means let him move out your things, and replace them with his own. Then, make your point eloquently and succinctly by continuing to carry out your excretory business in the file drawer that occupies the place where your litterbox used to be – and will soon be again, believe you me.

Number Seven. In the Fullness of Time, Prepare to Show Other New Additions Who Is Boss. In spite of your best efforts to prevent it, your female pet may eventually give indications that her breeding instincts have been aroused. The telltale signs include: phone conversations with her friends, in which the phrase "biological clock" crops up once every three sentences; hours spent browsing through the Sears catalogue with particular reference to the nursery section; suddenly turning your erstwhile undefiled domain into a regular Open House for every stray mother-and-toddler combination in the entire town.

This last manifestation, of course, is the one that really affects you. But a wise cat can turn even these occasional sticky-fingered invasions of drooling tykes into a benefit, by treating them as practice for the inevitable day when at least one infant human arrives on the scene as a permanent army of occupation.

Keep visiting babies in their place by stealing their toys and substituting something tattered and soiled from your own collection of playthings. Stare stonily into their faces when they attempt to smile at you with toothless incomprehension. Repeatedly rehearse making a dignified retreat, against the day when you are confronted by a rapidly crawling baby with molestation on his mind.

Unfortunately, there is nothing that can prepare you adequately for the unavoidable usurpation of your supremely central position in the household, which is going to occur when something warmer, noisier, and even more tyrannical than you takes up residence.

Although their litters are usually small, humans have a fierce if baffling predilection for the young of their own species, and a cat simply must learn to fight for the undivided attention that was heretofore his by common consent. Regrettably, you will have to learn to regard the palmy days of yore as firmly and irretrievably in the past.

No longer expect your pets to come bounding to the door to greet you when you return home from a hard day under the neighbor's porch, not when they've been up half the night with a teething kid. Forever behind you, also, is your female's endearing habit of clinging to whatever narrow portion of the bed you elect to allot her at night. Now what little sleep she gets is in the baby's room, dozing upright in a chair.

As for your male pet, who has gradually won you over with his sprightly tricks – no more will he delight in fetching, over and over again, the bits of crumpled cellophane you bat into the corners for him, or revel in the excitement of trying to grasp the lengths of string you wiggle so temptingly on the floor. It seems he'd rather be making a nuisance of himself in the nursery, standing guard over the baby in a loyal but exceedingly pointless way.

And yet, in spite of all the drawbacks and occasional heartaches, pet ownership is still a unique and rewarding experience that few cats ever regret having undertaken. Undoubtedly you will come to feel exactly the same way, especially if you adhere to the rules outlined above, and consequently come to enjoy to the fullest the close bond that exists between human beings and our more highly evolved species.

Great Expectations

Whenever people tell me how lucky I am to have a vivid imagination, I have to agree with them. Sort of. If truth be told, I'd far rather have a Swiss bank account, long blonde hair, or an extended vacation in a hot climate. But failing all of those, I guess an ability to imagine them accurately is the next best thing.

It's only in recent years, however, that I've come round to such a philosophical viewpoint on the entire question. In the early part of my life (as opposed to now, a period to which I euphemistically refer as "not-quite-so-early"), it often looked to me as though possessing an active sense of fantasy was about as uncomfortable (and just about as difficult to get rid of) as a case of plantar warts.

At the age of about eleven, for example, I rode to and from school every day on an imaginary horse named Hightail, much to the agonized consternation of my older brother, whom I would pass on the street corner, red-faced and mute with embarrassment, as Hightail and I galloped past him and a group of his derisive friends.

Pleading with my mother to make me give up my humiliating fantasy availed him nothing. My mother came down foursquare on the side of Creativity, Imagination, and Harmless Fun – all the extravagant rationales, in other words, that have been proffered as excuses for the embarrassing excesses of little sisters since time immemorial.

Eventually, therefore, my brother was compelled to take the law into his own hands. Determined to silence the guffaws of his friends, he came upon me one evening currying my horse beside the garage where I kept him stabled, and asked in a casual way if I would pinpoint for him exactly where the animal stood. Then, when I obliged, my brother produced an ancient bee-bee gun from behind his back and shot poor Hightail, who fell down as dead as any flesh-and-blood stallion would.

It was possibly fantasy's darkest but most impressive hour.

Sobered by the obvious hazards of imaginary-horse husbandry, I tried moving on to the next logical obsession for a girl of my age, which was the desire to become a movie star. It didn't seem to make the slightest difference that, in the clutches of a slow-blooming adolescence and as lank and gawky as a garden rake, the only title role for which I would readily qualify would be as *The Young and the Breastless*.

With a species of calm assurance I had never felt before or – believe me – since about anything, I wrote systematic letters to the major Hollywood studios, notifying them that I was available to consider any reasonable offer. In order to flesh out my scanty résumé, I wrote plays (bad plays) about plucky orphans, starring myself in pigtails and a navy felt hat with a streaming ribbon, along with whatever friends I could coerce into grudgingly taking up some of the more thankless supporting roles in the modern repertoire.

Initially, when the movie studios, including my personal favorite, Warner Brothers, sent me back only form letters thanking me for my interest and apprising me of their upcoming releases, I remained undiscouraged in my dream. Even when my lacklustre friends had stopped showing up for the rehearsals I called, I refused to give up, and I remember loftily informing my mother (no longer quite so firmly on the side of Creativity, Imagination, and Harmless Fun) that I couldn't possibly have my hair cut short, because when Hollywood called with a plum period role, I wanted to be ready with flowing tresses.

Finally, when it became abundantly clear even to me that stardom was not about to come knocking, I compromised at least to the extent of putting the fantasy on hold. Perhaps today was not the day, and maybe child stardom was not in the cards. But some day I was going to make it, that was for sure. (It sounded like the sort of thing the Plucky Orphan would say, at any rate.) A little bitterly, I trudged downtown to the hairdresser to get my hair lopped short.

Looking back on it, I don't really believe my penchant for unrealistic expectations was entirely my own fault. Some of it, I'm sure, had to do with growing up on the prairies, whose prosaic expanses positively insist on the aid of imagination in a way that makes the inspirational value of Venice and Samarkand seem feeble by comparison.

For another thing, I have spent most of my life being severely myopic. Believe me, when one is unable from the age of eight onward to see more than four inches in front of one's face without the detested assistance of a pair of glasses, one pretty much has to make up the world as one goes along.

(This is a statement of fact, by the way, not a plea for pity. I don't want you thinking that you're likely to come upon an ad in a magazine some day, touchingly describing my condition by means of a stark black-and-white snapshot of a squinting urchin, under-lined by a heart-rending caption: "Today Little Erika Will Walk Right Past Her Best Friend and Attempt to Make Conversation with a Golfbag, Unless You Are Prepared to Help.")

The world I made up was basically a pretty cosmetically appeal-ing place. I was sixteen before I realized that my front teeth had a space between them, by which time the gap had already begun to close. I went all through grade school with no idea that my favorite teacher had a web of exploded veins across her cheeks, a receded hairline, and dark sweat-stains in the armpits of all her dresses. And I never met a dog I didn't like, simply because the dogs I met never looked runny-eyed, toothless, swaybacked, or mangy.

Nevertheless, my fantasy life took a sharp and deviant turn by the time I reached high school age, when I came under the tutelage of a convent full of nuns who, as we know, are not as a group particularly sympathetic to flights of fancy unless they happen to include godly peasants with stigmata, statues coming to life, saintly bodies that don't decompose, letter-openers carved from bits of the True Cross, or the Blessed Virgin appearing to large groups of the devout, none of whom has had the foresight to bring along a camera.

Imaginings of a more secular kind the Sisters had no use for, and I quickly learned the folly of throwing notes out the convent window that read, "Help, I'm being held prisoner by a gang of white-slavers. Notify the police." Or sneaking downtown to see The Great Reveen hypnotize the entire audience of the Capitol Theatre into believing they were chickens, or painting my finger-nails green in emulation of Sally Bowles in *I Am a Camera*.

What the nuns did put stock in, however, almost as ferociously as they believed in the Mystery of the Trinity, was the tremendous importance of a high school education; and the riches that would accrue from it was a fantasy they actively encouraged. To the extent that Graduation was an event for which they began to prepare us at least three years in advance by assuring us, on an almost daily basis, of how remote our individual chances were of ever making it up to that sublime dais in a mortarboard and gown.

The fate of a girl who did not Graduate (or choose the veil) was, apparently, terrible indeed. She became a hairdresser – or worse. What the nuns' idea of worse was, we never did find out specifi-cally, although there were very definite indications that it included tragic associations with a class of persons for whom Sunday Mass was not necessarily a foregone conclusion.

But from the girls' point of view, the most terrifying aspect of failure to Graduate was not the moral decay that would rapidly and inevitably follow; it was the awful prospect of not getting to go to the Graduation Prom.

Like the grade twelve final examinations themselves, the Prom was something a prudent girl planned ahead for right from grade nine onward, so that there was no possibility of her being caught short on the night with a dress that had been anything less than a year in the designing, or a date that had been arranged on anything tighter than six months' notice.

As far as the date end of it went, the policy of many girls was to select a boyfriend as early as grade nine or ten, and just hang onto him for as many years as it took to get to the Prom. Otherwise, there was the awful risk of winding up going with somebody's cousin from Estevan, or else joining an amorphous party of life's losers, male and female, to spend the evening dancing with a variety of unattractive rejects, not one of whom had shelled out for your corsage.

I, with typical irresponsibility, didn't get around to worrying about the Prom until about the middle of grade eleven, by which time it was almost too late. I had nothing in the way of accumulated male resources to fall back on. After all, I was still spending my Friday nights in the library and my Saturday nights in front of old reruns of *The Untouchables* instead of out at school dances stalking promising quarry. With the result that, after almost three years in an exclusively female atmosphere, I didn't even know any boys by name, except my brother, who had never quite recovered from the Hightail episode and was still not speaking to me on a regular basis.

So paralysed was I by the prospect of having to be "fixed up" for the Prom the following year that I let almost another twelve months go by before I leapt into action.

It was after Christmas of my final year in high school, with a scant four months in which to get lucky, that I began attending dances both at my own school and at neighboring collegiates in a regular dreary ritual of looking for a stone as yet unturned, from beneath which something more or less two-legged might possibly come crawling to escort me to the Prom.

What can I say? I snapped up the first one who was discernibly human. He had blond hair, a nice smile (in spite of braces), and access to a car. Beyond that, I didn't know and didn't care. I was on my way to the Prom.

Unfortunately, having made my move in early February, I still had three interminable months of weekly dates to log in with my "boyfriend" (my God, it felt like something that was happening to someone else) before Graduation rolled around in May.

We had some scintillating times. I was interested in English Literature; the one subject he expected to pass was Physics. He was a fan of the Black Hawks; the only inhabitant of Chicago I knew anything about was Al Capone. I believed in Free Love; he had heard from the priests at his school that even petting was a mortal sin.

That last was the real rub – or lack of rub, if you want to look at it like that. The way the nuns always told it, boys were dying to get into girls' pants, and the only effective method of preventing it was to "reach for the doorhandle, as soon as he reaches for the ignition key". Any automobile, in other words, that was not rolling along the road at a minimum of twenty miles an hour was a near occasion of sin, and a girl's task was to keep her boyfriend (more sexually inclined, and therefore less able to help himself) from the insatiable urge to park.

Parking was fine with me. My face having cleared up somewhat (although since I still refused to wear my glasses, I couldn't tell for sure) and my recent discovery of black eyeliner having changed my appearance from the unappealingly mousy to the moodily raccoonlike, I looked forward to the prospect of fending off the sweaty-palmed advances of a man driven mad by my beauty.

Unfortunately, my boyfriend was not that man. Or at least he was somehow managing to keep those legendary male sexual inclinations in check without any help from me. It was humiliating. All those years of being primed to believe that my virtue was something I was going to have to fight for continually, and here I was, the first time out, practically begging him to take advantage.

But as a member of the Sodality of the Blessed Virgin (a crack squad of pious Catholic kamikazes too depressing to describe) he was adamantly determined to keep us both on the straight and narrow, even if it meant having nothing else to fill our interminable dating time with except those limping Black Hawk–Capone conversations and a few chaste kisses now and again. However, just to make sure I understood no personal slight was intended, he asked me, almost as an afterthought, if I wanted to go steady.

Frankly, I thought steady was exactly what we *had* been going all this time. What I wanted to go was crazy for a change. Tight-lipped, I declined his ring, which he put back into his pocket with a philosophical shrug I have since learned is a common male gestural equivalent of "Women, who can figure 'em?" Still, steady or no steady, week after week our dating continued as the clock inched, with infinitesimal slowness, ever Promward.

Chances are I would have been raving screaming mad by April, and therefore free of any continued concern about the Prom, had not fantasy – as usual – reared its giddy head with a seductive siren song on its grinning lips that sounded, to me at least, like the promising anthem that was going to save the day.

The fantasy took the corporeal form of a mop-topped (an archaic adjective dating from the Early Beatle Era) boy of the British persuasion (about the trendiest thing one could be in the E.B.E., particularly in Saskatchewan) whom I met one day in the record department of Simpson's, where he worked on Saturdays and after school.

That was all. I met him, spoke to him momentarily over some purchase I was making (Early Beatles is a safe bet), and by the time I found myself transported out of Simpson's on a cloud of delight and the Down escalator, I was in love.

Not only was I in love, I was determined to defy the stars, shock good society, and hang the consequences by appearing at the Prom with my English moppet (likely not Catholic, and therefore full of sexual promise) instead of that paragon of Christian forbearance that I'd been enduring every Saturday night for the past two months.

All that was required to attain my object, as far as I could see, was to begin frequenting Simpson's on a daily basis armed with some snappy *badinage*, an abundance of blue eye-shadow, and a convincing interest in new hit recordings, and let Nature take its course.

Nature did take its course, as Nature always does, but unfortunately in this case it turned out that Nature's plans and mine in no way coaligned. Try as I would, badinaging snappily, batting my blue-lidded eyes, and talking music, music, music non-stop, I still could not get that boy even remotely interested in the subject of my Prom.

His school, he allowed when grilled on the subject, was having a Prom too. But he showed no inclination to ask me to it. Nor did he manifest any curiosity as to whether I intended to go to my own, and with whom. In England, it seemed, the tradition of the Grad Prom did not exist – which may have been his oblique way of saying he saw no reason why it should be flourishing in the New World.

At this point, I was inclined to agree with him, and I found myself wondering more and more if there might still be time for me to immigrate to Britain and establish myself in a new life before Prom Night rolled around, some two weeks hence. Really, it did seem preferable to dealing with the excruciating torment of going out to face the most momentous evening of my life on the arm of a Man I Did Not Love while the Man I Did Love either whirled, uncaring, around the floor of his school gym with some other girl, or else spent the evening among the record stock at Simpson's, taking inventory of Accordion Classics.

To spare you unbearable suspense, gentle reader, I will tell you that in the end I went to the Prom with my boyfriend as planned, and hated every minute of it. When he showed up at my house, his parents' car freshly washed in honor of the occasion, I barely looked at the corsage of orchids he brought me (the English moppet, I knew, would have brought baby roses).

Nor did I really listen as he did a double-take, then exclaimed at how amazing I looked, although I knew that, my hair done up in masses of ringlet curls and sprayed silver, I was as close as I was ever going to get to appearing regal. But what was the point of such queenly magnificence when the king of my heart was otherwise engaged, and the only other guy on deck was a joker who was clearly having problems coming to terms with what I'd done to my hair?

By the time we'd dropped over to his place, so that his mother could take in my hoary splendiferousness and snap a few commemorative shots of the occasion, I was practically speechless with misery, as well as furious with myself for systematically ruining my big night with bootless fantasies.

All those months of desperate planning and endless tedious dates, not to mention the countless hours spent picking the Dress, and replaying the picking of the Dress with other girls who had picked Dresses too. The exultation of having outfoxed destiny by escaping the necessity of spending Prom Night dateless, as I'd secretly feared for years. The joyous high school memories that were supposed to culminate in this one stupendous event...all of it sabotaged by my fretful yearning for what I couldn't get.

As I described listless circles around the gym – decorated with paper flowers forming the words "Welcome to our Porm" which had been painstakingly hung by a decorating committee with more zeal than talent for orthography – I imagined myself in the arms of my uncooperative English moppet and how, on the sidelines, my classmates would whisper speculation among themselves.

"Where did she find him?" "I've never seen him before, and what a doll!" "Did you catch the cute accent?" "That wily girl. To think she's only been going out with the dolt all this time as a cover!"

On my bare back, I could feel the warm pressure of my boyfriend's fingers, moist and urgent. He was having the time of

his life and, now that he'd recovered from the initial shock of my
silver curls, was actually very proud to be seen with me. Why?
Considering that I was an ungracious, sullen, and unhappy girl,
who was at this very moment reviling him in her imagination.

Instead of driving straight home, blissful, amorous, and just a
little drunk at almost 3 a.m., he took an unscheduled detour into
the park, drew up beside the lake, reached for the ignition key,
and turned the engine off.

"Hey, wait a sec," I said, in the longest sentence I'd spoken to
him all night. "What's the big – ?"

The kiss he pressed against my mouth was hot and promising,
and was swiftly followed up by an eager hand leaping into the
neckline of the Dress like a porpoise. With a sensation as close to
tragic irony as one can feel at seventeen, I realized that here, at
last, was the action so long begged for and so vociferously denied.

"Now, look." I pushed him away and pressed his exploratory
hand firmly onto the car seat between us. "What are the other
guys in Sodality going to say?"

The devil-may-care expression that crossed his face might
actually have struck me as funny had I been in a less wretched
mood. "Who cares what they say? It's Grad Prom Night, right?"

"Right," I said wearily. "Look, if it's all the same to you, I'd like
to go home."

If I'd reached across the seat to pour a handful of hot nickels
down the front of his trousers, he couldn't have looked more
surprised. "Home? Holy jeez, this is a switch. What's the matter
with you tonight?"

I tried to rouse myself to make the effort to explain that it was
simply too late in the evening – not to mention the day – for X-
rated overtures, but my mouth was too tired to form the words.

"Home," I repeated instead. "Please."

At my parents' front door, he made a last stab at kindling my
ardor by kissing me fervently and whispering in my ear that
tonight had been the happiest evening he'd ever spent.

Successfully resisting the urge to whisper back that it just went
to show, didn't it, how very different people could be, I gave his
hand an ambiguous little squeeze, then hurriedly unlocked the
front door and disappeared into the house. Forever.

Because by the time I'd even turned my key in the lock ("By the time he reaches for the ignition key, you reach for the . . . "), I'd made my mind up to one unequivocal fact: I was never going out with him again.

There was no earthly need to, really. Like a drone bee, he'd fulfilled his biological function by taking me to the Prom, and now that his job was finished, I – the queen, regal in my metallic coiffure – was going to expel him from the hive. That was all. Not so much cruel. Not insensitive. Just Nature taking its course once again – only this time, Nature's agenda and mine agreed.

The next day (or a little later the same day, I guess it was) when he called me, I wasn't in. When he called back later still, I was in but unavailable. The next day, when he finally got me on the phone, I was still unavailable – remote and uncommunicative. A few days later, when my Graduation exercises rolled around, I didn't invite him. When he invited me to his, I failed to show.

At that point, he took the hint and never bothered me again.

As for the Man I Loved, the English mop-top, I never attempted to look him up again either, although I continued to resent for a long long time the way he'd spoiled my Grad Prom, and to this day, the sound of an English accent automatically makes me feel thwarted.

Perhaps not too surprisingly, after the whole unhappy episode, and once I got over feeling thoroughly ashamed of myself, I made a determined effort to expunge the destructive effects of fantasy from my life. No more, I declared, was I going to fret my time away, pining for that which was clearly unavailable at the obvious expense of that which was. From now on, I was firmly and solely on the side of that which I could get. (Although I made a brief note to myself to try harder to ensure that what I got was of somewhat higher quality to begin with.)

The fact that I was leaving high school at this point and heading on to university in Montreal would, I knew, help immeasurably in assisting me in sticking to these laudable resolves. After all, wasn't I entering into that halcyon period of one's life in which, it could honestly be said, reality was up to one's expectations?

Whatever truth there was in the adage was not immediately apparent in my first few months on campus, which consisted of a succession of Saturday nights spent in the basement common room of the women's residence watching old movies on TV with the rest of the not-yet-established. The recollection of a gang of nightgowned young women – our hair in curlers and many of us overweight from the starchy residence food combined with our frequent compensatory doses of machine-dispensed chocolate, our knitting needles clicking furiously as we wept over Terence Stamp in *Billy Budd* – is something I am not likely ever to forget, although therapy has helped immensely.

Eventually, however, I did get myself out of the residence basement and into the swing of university life, with the result that, after several false starts and missed cues, I found myself embroiled in a relationship that really did merit the epithet "love affair", and which was, I firmly believed, based on the principle of reality over fantasy.

Of course, I was cheating it just a little bit by having found someone whose background and qualifications fulfilled quite adequately the sort of ivy-covered East Coast fantasies that are possibly peculiar to prairie-bred girls.

He was from a background redolent of military academies, summers in Europe, tea dances, and trips to the Cape – the rock-ribbed stuff of the J. P. Marquand novels to which I was, in those days, imbecilically addicted. My role, meanwhile, had been penned by another writer in a novel called *Kitty Foyle*, whose perfect modern counterpart I saw myself as being. Miss Nobody from No Place, versus the entire Eastern establishment. It was a match made, if not in heaven, at least on the back lot of Warner Brothers.

Although I was myself perfectly satisfied to leave the vast social gulf between us as a strictly theoretical entity, there came the day when he announced that I must come down home with him one weekend to meet the family, who lived several hours' drive (but not nearly far enough to suit me) south of Montreal. Full of trepidation and the delightfully scary knowledge that this encounter could make or break me, I consented to come along for the ride.

The family homestead was a little less grand than I'd expected, but still a great deal grander than my family's tract-house bungalow on its fifty-foot lot back in Regina. The family itself consisted of: a couple of younger brothers who seemed openly resentful that a very popular former girlfriend of their big brother's had been dropped summarily to make way for me; a taciturn father who appeared to disapprove of me on more general principles; and an imminently senile grandmother who played only one emotion – vast indifference – but played it very well. This effusive welcome into the bosom of my (I hoped) future family I had been prepared for, particularly the grandmother's sniffy hauteur. Grandmother was the dowager empress who had risen from humbler circumstances to marry into this fine old manufacturing family about a hundred and forty years before, and she was, therefore, naturally sensitive to the advent of other low-class interlopers.

Father, for his part, was also still nursing a grudge (I later learned) over the ouster of the last girlfriend – Mayflower descendant, both sides! – in favor of Sunbonnet Nell from up Canada way, who wore too much eyeliner and kept squinting at her dinner.

But, in fact, on this occasion it wasn't my myopia that was responsible for such anxious peering – it was the dinner itself. Lobster. My very first lobster, lying on the plate, beady-eyed and malevolent as a giant cockroach, and just about as appetizing.

Surely we weren't expected to eat this thing. How on earth did one even approach it? The set of nutcrackers and small prising instruments that lay beside my plate seemed, to my inexperienced eye, to have nothing at all to do with the red armor-plating and gruesome twitching antennae of the monster glaring up from the table, daring me to make the first move. I'd have as soon eaten a tangle of baling wire.

Plainly, however, my opinion was not shared by anyone else at the table. The entire family – boys, father, and haughty gran – were all murmuring exclamations of approval at the size and anticipated quality of the lobsters the housekeeper had set down at each place and were reaching eagerly for their implements and bowls of drawn butter in expectation of the joy to come.

Covertly (and myopically) I glanced around me to see how the assault on the shell was mounted. The nutcrackers, it seemed, were applied to selected parts of the beast, which shattered smartly under the pressure like so many bloodshot Brazil nuts.

With a feeling that could be described as cautious pessimism, I picked up an inert claw and pressed it gingerly with the nutcracker. Bang! There was a sharp report like a gunshot, then a shard of claw went flying off my plate, whizzed into a wall, and caromed off the corner of the china cabinet before clattering noisily to the floor directly behind Gran's chair.

No one else appeared to notice. Resolutely, the entire clan continued to crack their lobsters neatly, dip the meat in melted butter, and devour it with pleasure, just as though the sounds of heavy artillery shelling were not reverberating from my place at the table.

Humiliated but driven by the desire to succeed, I doggedly continued shattering my lobster with the nutcracker, and random pieces of shell parts continued to ricochet about the room. The younger brothers, I could perceive blurrily, were smirking at me, while my own true love – who'd got me into this mess in the first place – sucked blissfully on the disgusting little legs of his second lobster, steadfastly ignoring my plight.

What the patriarch of the family must have been thinking I could only imagine, although this was one time I preferred to leave the realm of fanciful speculation strictly alone. Besides, irrespective of what was going through his mind, one thing and one thing alone was perfectly clear, even to a woman as short-sighted and blinded by her own embarrassed tears as I: the debut of the latter-day Kitty Foyle was a complete and unequivocal flop.

Just as I was trying to make up my mind whether to rush away in a flood of tears, or merely sink underneath the table for the rest of the meal, Grandmother unexpectedly laid down her lobster tools and leaned over to speak in my ear.

"Don't you mind about it," she said. "They did the same damn thing to me, sixty years ago, the first time I came to dinner in this house and had never seen a lobster."

In all the time I knew her, it was the only utterance the woman addressed to me, even though I survived the lobster dinner to go on to marry her grandson. But through all the successive years of her protracted silences, I continued to feel that if Grandmother did have only one thing to say to me, at least she had chosen her moment admirably.

This would, of course, be the point at which to tell you that, sobered by my introduction to my future husband's family, and weighted down by the subsequent responsibilities of matrimony, I gave over the world of make-believe altogether, but I'm afraid such is not the case.

Over the years, in fact, in spite of all my high school resolutions about giving over that type of thing, I have noted in myself a marked increase in the degree to which I tend to romanticize my life.

I don't think it's quite so much that my existence has been such an absolute bust that it requires continual imaginative improvement (although it's been no picnic either, make no mistake about that). Rather, my current tendency is to blame the craft of writing for the necessity of relying on fantastical speculation to get me through the day.

In my line, I depend enormously on my imagination – not to assist me in my work, of course, which I make every effort to render as flat and prosaic as possible, but instead to help me through the infinitely trickier and more taxing business of simply being a writer.

For example, if I expect to justify an endless succession of entire afternoons spent staring moodily into space as something called "working", then I'm obliged to arm myself with a few ready explanations of what exactly it is that I'm doing.

Watching out the window as a man attempts repeatedly and unsuccessfully to parallel-park in a space that wouldn't accommodate a grocery cart falls under the heading of "Observations, Life", and I might, just by way of substantiation, even go to the lengths of making the odd note on it. Should I pause, however, in mid-note to gaze wistfully at the dirt under a fingernail for fifteen minutes or more at a stretch, then there's an imaginary job description to cover that activity too. I call it "Observations, Personal", and I fully expect that the resulting piece – tentatively titled "Thoughts on Grime: a Thumbnail Sketch" – is something I will be making a start on any day now.

Additionally, the ability merely to fantasize writing itself as a glamorous occupation stands me in good stead, I find, whether it's a trip to the accountant with a manila envelope stuffed with restaurant receipts, bills from Grand and Toy, and CBC pay stubs all jumbled together, or an invitation to ride the streetcar out to

Mimico to address the Friends of Literature, who, it turns out, actually requested Margaret Atwood and aren't a bit pleased that I've turned up instead.

Besides which, when it really comes down to it, I do believe at some level in the general efficacy of fantasy itself, as evidenced by a bright redemptive moment I experienced a few years ago that serves as well as anything I can think of to offer hope for the future, as well as vindicate the wistful dreams of the past.

I happened to find myself, one day, in California looking for a parking space on the Warner-Columbia lot, where I had some business to transact – the kind of business that comes into every writer's life sooner or later, regardless of how clean one tries to keep one's nose.

Worried that I'd put the rental car too near a fire hydrant, I glanced around nervously for a policeman, before suddenly realizing that where I'd parked was not a real city street, but a set, in which everything, right down to the fire hydrant, was made of painted wood. The only cop, therefore, who would be likely to approach would be a fake one, flashing a fake badge before writing me out a fake summons.

No sooner was I laughing at that fanciful notion than I realized something else, something so astounding that it took my breath away. I had made it. Twenty years late, and still no star on the dressing-room door, but I had made it, none the less.

To the same Warner Brothers studios to which I'd written with calm little-girl conviction all those years ago, knowing that somehow, some day, it was all going to be for real. And here I was. Just as I always knew I would be. Score it Fantasy, One; Reality, Nothing.